Healing with Real Food

Dr Neal Loh

Integrative Veterinarian

This is the first edition published in 2023.

ISBN: 978-0-6458318-0-1

All correspondence should be addressed to:

Dr. Neal Loh

neal@holisticpetvet.com.au

Website: www.holisticpetvet.com.au

Perth, Western Australia

Disclaimer

The information in this book comes from a combination of referenced texts as well as the author's personal experience and observation in his patients. It is designed to guide pet owners feed a diet that is most appropriate according to their pets' needs. TCVM food therapy serves as a tool to heal and any changes to dietary requirements should be reviewed at least once annually. Always consult with your integrative veterinarian for advice on any health conditions.

About the author

Dr. Neal Loh

BSc BVMS CVA CVCH CVFT

Dr. Neal Loh grew up in Singapore and pursued veterinary studies through Murdoch University in Perth, Western Australia. He is also affectionately known as Choon Kiat, or Ah Kiat during his younger schooling years. Neal has worked in various private clinics and hospitals for five years prior starting his own Perth-based practice specialising in integrative and holistic veterinary medicine – **Holistic Pet Vet**. He obtained post-graduate certifications in veterinary acupuncture, Chinese herbal medicine and food therapy from Chi University in Florida, USA. Neal has also given several lectures on integrative medicine at the veterinary nursing institution. He has also appeared on a local radio talk show and video podcast. Neal lives with his loving wife (Jeri), three children, two Maine Coon cats and a Mini-Lop rabbit. Outside of work, he spends his time gardening, trail walking and coaching at the local junior soccer club.

In year 2020, Neal and Jeri founded **Holitreats** *(www.holitreats.com.au)* – one-stop online store where you will find plenty of natural treats, dental chews, specialty nutritional supplements, essential oil blends and aromatherapy products for companion pets.

TABLE OF CONTENTS

1. USING THIS BOOK

This book was written solely for pet parents and veterinarians to understand the value of appropriate nutrition in bettering the health of companion animals. I have narrowed down and translated core principles of Chinese Medicine into succinct chapters. They reflect my deeper understanding and subsequent application in veterinary medicine as a modern practitioner. Having some fundamental knowledge in Chinese Medicine helps us to fine tune our perception of a dog's nutritional needs, especially when we consider all other aspects of health, adding immense value to the already exceptional diet.

By the end of this book, you will be able to formulate a diet using a variety of foods to create the ultimate balanced diet for your dog's needs. I have included a quick reference *food energetics guide* that will enable you to quickly select appropriate foods.

The final few chapters are examples of transitional diets that you can adapt for common conditions such as inflammatory bowel disease, recurring ear infections, kidney disease and cancers. It is designed to help pet parents move away from a commercial dry diet, reduce reliance on medications and hopefully improve health outcomes.

2. THE JOURNEY

In our modern society where science and technology seemed so advanced that we have a well-stocked pharmacy to treat most acute symptoms, we lack fundamental knowledge in nutrition and preventive health. In face of degenerative ailments, kidney impairment for instance, we tend to adopt a wait-and-see approach, only to start treatment when the affected organ deteriorates. We seemed to have moved away from the very systems and traditions that has worked and benefitted generations.

During my years in general practice as a small animal veterinarian, I quickly realised many of the dilemmas, challenges and limitations of modern medicine. Many patients had either recurring symptoms or are "just not right". Digestion related disorders and skin allergies were high up on the list. Dogs presenting with symptoms were getting younger, even as young as four months old puppies who cannot seem to digest food properly.

The long-term dietary solution for these dogs is often a specialised, low fat or hydrolysed protein dry kibble diet. However, the solution for health and well-being is far from being that straightforward. I wished! For many of you reading this, including veterinarians, will hopefully have seen that specialised dry diets only curb the symptoms temporarily. Most dogs will also often present with multiple symptoms in various areas such as digestion, skin and behavioral.

My journey towards an integrative and holistic veterinarian started with Traditional Chinese Medicine (TCM). Growing up in Singapore with a strong eastern cultural influence, eating appropriate foods in moderation and drinking herbal decoctions were common, especially in preventing the onset of a cold. It became a part of me. I only remembered going to the doctor's twice in my childhood, and one of those visits was for an acute appendicitis (which unfortunately quickly spiraled downwards and became a surgical case).

In the first seven years upon graduation from vet school, I completed post-graduate certifications in Veterinary Acupuncture, Chinese Herbal Medicine and Food Therapy. I started treating patients using both western and eastern medicine. The results were phenomenal. Harnessing the power from both medicines; pharmaceutical drugs were deployed for acute symptoms whilst using dietary modifications to address root causes. In the early stages of my career, empowering pet owners with the knowledge of using appropriate fresh wholesome foods was the best tool I ever had.

There was less urgency to see my patients frequently as they began to rely less on medications. Increase in mood, energy and shinier hair coats were the other positive outcomes of making minor adjustments using fresh foods. Dogs were more emotionally connected to their owners. I will always be grateful to all the dedicated pet parents for entrusting their furry companions' health into my hands, also for bettering my knowledge every day.

Interestingly, my first patient I treated with acupuncture was a kitten. At only eleven months old, Demon (his actual name) had dislocated his sacrum from a minor car accident. There were no other fractures or internal injuries. The only problem was that he could not urinate nor stand with his hind legs. He had been in hospital for 3 days already at that time and the inability to urinate is a potentially life-threatening condition. After the first session of acupuncture, Demon urinated on his own by the next day, and subsequently started putting weight on his hind legs within the same week. Fast forward two more sessions, he got discharged from hospital and on my last visit to him he had jumped onto the kitchen bench to steal food!

Demon affirmed my beliefs and proved that there are so much more possibilities to the doctrine of veterinary science. The rest is history. Here I am, writing this book on this day to share my experience and knowledge.

3. CANINE BIOLOGICAL DIETS

As veterinarians we often get asked about what the best type of food is to feed our dogs. Before we try to answer that question it's best to let us understand the biological diets of canids.

Regardless of the breed of dog, Schnauzers, Maltese, Terriers, Mastiffs, Retrievers, Shepherds, and the list goes on, the jaw anatomy, dentition and gut microbiome remains vastly consistent. Noting similarities to wild canids such as wolves, the shape of their jaw with strong canines allows them to apprehend their prey, tear meat off the carcass and break the meal down in a step-by-step fashion. Feeding a specie appropriate diet entails an extremely rich source of mental enrichment, it is time consuming and can be also a tiring process.

Commercial dry and canned diets, on the other hand, provides very little engagement to a domesticated dog that that naturally thrives on instinctual habits like smelling, tasting foods with varying texture and tastes. Interestingly, a group of zoologists studied the nutrient profile of wild canids in comparison to domesticated dogs.[1] The gut contents of wild canids were studied and referred to as the ancestral diets. Domesticated dogs were given a free choice selection of various foods and was referred to as the instinctual diet.

The ancestral diet was found to contain 54% protein, 45% fat and 1% carbohydrate. When given a free choice (instinctual diet), the nutrient profile came to 30% protein, 63% fat and 9% carbohydrates. The bottom line is that the average canine's diet typically comprises of a moderate to high protein and fat ratio, with minimal carbohydrates. This begs the question: do dogs need carbohydrates? Do they actively seek out carbohydrates in the wild?

There is no biological requirement for carbohydrates. The 1% carbohydrate found in the ancestral diets is likely derived directly from the prey's stomach contents, from smaller mammals like rabbits and rodents. However, carbohydrates are excellent sources of energy. Studies have also shown that dogs (and cats) are actually very efficient at digesting and utilising carbohydrates, provided that they are already partially digested, cooked or processed in some way. This explains why commercial dry diets usually have carbohydrates in excess of 40%. This allows the energy requirements on label to be met using more affordable ingredients other than animal protein.

4. MODERN CANINE NUTRITIONAL STANDARDS

In this chapter I will help us understand nutritional standards that most commercial pet foods are based upon. I also want to dissect pet food labels and understand both the ingredients list and nutrient profile.

You will see a lot on commercial diets that are nutritionally balanced and adhere to the AAFCO standards[2] or NRC guidelines. AAFCO stands for Association of American Feed Control Officials. NRC stands for National Research Council[3]. AAFCO sets nutrient standards and labelling requirement for commercial pet food products.

In the past few decades, we are also seeing more commercial pet foods being advertised as using natural ingredients or made with real meat. The shift is mainly driven by consumers' demands and expectations as pet owners gear towards a more natural diet. To satisfy AAFCO's definition and labelling pet food as "natural", ingredients must not contain any artificial preservatives or colouring, with exception for minerals and vitamins which can be synthetic.

Definitions

Reading pet food labels can be confusing. What do some of the terms mean? Here are some of the words you may come across.

1. *Poultry = Whole or part of carcass +/- bones. Without feathers, head, feet and internal organs.*
2. *Poultry meal = Part of carcass +/- bones. Without feathers, head, feet and internal organs.*
3. *Poultry by-products = neck, feet, internal organs, without feathers.*

4. *Meat meal and by-products = mammal without hair, hoof, hide, rumen and stomach contents.*

Guaranteed Analysis

Guaranteed analysis from a food label simply tells us the breakdown of nutrients, in percentages, such as fat, protein, carbohydrates, fibre, etc. It also tells us the energy density of the particular food product, meaning the amount of calories it carries per kilogram (kcal/kg). Because of the differences in energy density between two products, comparing using guaranteed analysis alone is inaccurate[4]. For instance, a product that says 5% fat may not always be lower in fat as compared to another product stating 8% fat.

Using the energy density (kcal/kg) and percentages, we can estimate the actual weight of each component when consumed, such as protein and fat. This is calculating based on caloric basis, which is more reliable than just plain percentages. It allows us to compare apples to apples. It is also important to note that presence of any moisture, such as in dog rolls or canned food, will also have a significant impact. Caloric basis is expressed in grams (of fat/protein) per Mcal.

Using real examples of common commercial pet food products:

Guaranteed Analysis	*Kangaroo Dog Roll*	*Low Fat Digestive Dry Kibble*
Energy density (Kcal/kg)	1125	3311
Protein %	10	26.1
Fat %	3	7.5

To estimate the caloric density of protein and fat:

Step 1: Add 1.5% to protein, or 1% to fat

Step 2: Divide energy density by 10,000

Step 3: Take the value in step 1 and divide by the value in step 2.

The simple reason behind adding 1.5% to protein and 1% to fat is due to the average concentration differences between guaranteed and actual measured analysis of nutrients[4]. This helps increase the accuracy of our nutrient estimation.

Estimating caloric density	*Kangaroo Dog Roll*	*Low Fat Digestive Dry Kibble*
Protein	10% + 1.5% = 11.5% 1125/10000 = 0.1125 11.5/0.1125 = 102.2 g/Mcal	26.1% + 1.5% = 27.6% 3311/10000 = 0.3311 27.6/0.3311 = 83.4 g/Mcal
Fat	**3%** + 1% = 4% 1125/10000 = 0.1125 4/0.1125 = **35.5 g/Mcal**	**7.5%** + 1% = 8.5% 3311/10000 = 0.3311 8.5/0.3311 = **25.7 g/Mcal**

Let's look at fat content between the two diets. According to the guaranteed analysis, the dry kibble appears to have twice as much fat as compared to the kangaroo roll. The caloric density proves that we can never compare two products based on guaranteed analysis alone. Understanding this concept may come in handy when selecting a suitable low-fat commercial food product for conditions such as pancreatitis.

5. BASIC PRINCIPLES OF TRADITIONAL CHINESE MEDICINE (TCM)

In order to utilise and apply food therapy effectively, we must first understand a few basic concepts of TCM. What I adore about Chinese Medicine is the recognition of individuality. Every one of us, including a dog, cat, or horse is unique. We all have our own differences, which means very few things in life can be "one-size-fits-all". Acupuncture, herbal therapy and any dietary choices must suit one's needs in order for them to work.

Note that this is different to allopathic medicine where the focus is on symptomatic treatment. Practitioners trained in modern medicine are taught to follow a protocol-type thought process to investigate, diagnose and treat accordingly. Having gone through the rigorous training in veterinary school myself, this method of diagnosis is extremely effective in matching symptoms with potential differential diseases. However, life never tends to be straightforward, especially in the area of health and medicine. It is common to see patients with non-specific symptoms and without a definitive diagnosis. Most notable examples in veterinary medicine are idiopathic epilepsy, fever of unknown origin, meningitis of unknown origin, irritable bowel syndrome, just to name a few.

Allopathic and Traditional medicine are like bread and bun, each are brilliant in their own way and cannot be compared side by side. They simply address health from different angles. Chinese Medicine addresses the root cause, not the disease, such that we can adopt a more proactive and preventive approach to health. To understand how our body is connected, we must first learn about the *Four Essential Substances* and the *Five Elements*. This will provide you with a fundamental knowledge to help connect the dots between seemingly unrelated symptoms such as anxiety and digestive disorders, or aggression and ear infections, etc.

i.   Four Essential Substances

Firstly, we must understand the concept of the four essential substances that exist in life and nature - *Qi, Blood, Yin* and *Yang*.

Qi & Blood

Qi refers to life force, and is generated by the body from food, as well as via respiration from the atmosphere (known as the *cosmic Qi*). Qi is also stored in our body as Jing (Essence), which keeps us alive and helps build our immune system so we can fend off pathogens and disturbances from climatic changes. Think of Jing as a type of fuel. Qi flows through each and every of our body systems; keeping our blood constantly circulating. Qi can never be in excess, however a deficiency in Qi may make us feel tired easily despite sufficient rest, or a poorer immune system with slow recoveries.

So why do we need Qi? It moves Blood. In TCM, the concept of Blood is much broader than our actual definition of the word blood. Notice the uppercase B when referring to Blood in TCM, and lowercase for actual blood. For instance, Blood deficiency does not necessarily mean anaemia, however if one's anaemic, he/she represents the later stages of Blood deficiency. One of the benefits of Chinese Medicine is the ability to pick up and prevent diseases, sometimes even before they become symptomatic. Blood deficiency can often present as intolerance to cold, having cool extremities, general weakness, pale complexion (humans), dry and cracked paw pads (dogs and cats), and haircoats with white flaky skin. These signs suggest the lack of Blood to circulate, warm and nourish appropriately. Think of it as a garden hose. Qi is the water pressure and Blood is the water within. Qi drives Blood, Blood carries Qi. A deficiency of either will often lead to deficiencies in both Qi and Blood if the root cause is left untreated.

Yin & Yang

Yin and Yang is a concept that reflects nature's way of balance and sustenance. They are two polar opposites in its energetic form and yet can be converted in either direction. Within the law of physics, energy is neither created or lost, it is merely transformed.

Most will be familiar with the Taoist symbol of Yin and Yang. "There will always be a little bit of yin in yang, and a little bit of yang in yin." Yin cannot exist without Yang, and Yang cannot exist without Yin. This is akin to day (Yang) and night (Yin). At dawn there is still some Yin and at dusk there is still some Yang. There cannot be daylight if night never existed. We can also apply this understanding onto various aspects of holistic health, foods and even personalities.

Yin is typically associated with cooling, moistening, being on the inside, introverted, darkness, quietness. There are herbs and foods that specifically nourishes Yin, such as pork, honey, asparagus, to name a few. Yang on the other hand, relates to warming, being on the outside, extroverted, brightness and loudness. Venison, mutton, dried ginger, garlic, rosemary, basil and thyme all nourishes Yang.

Yin and Yang must be balanced, for the body to remain in harmony and preservation of health. If Yin is depleted, from physical exhaustion, drug abuse, hormonal imbalances or inappropriate diets, then we have a seemingly excess Yang energy which translates to "false heat". Remember Yang is warming. Yin deficiency is a common form of imbalance we see in our society as well as in our companion pets. The false heat causes constant thirst and dryness, inability to sleep soundly through the night, nervousness, abnormal sweating and feeling hot all the time.

To tie the four substances together, it is helpful to remember that Qi and Blood are constantly circulating through every organ system, and each system stores its own reserves of Qi. Within each organ system there is also the balance of Yin and Yang to maintain homeostasis.

Using kidney impairment as an example to illustrate. Kidney disease refers to the deterioration of kidney function, which may sound like they occur similarly across individuals. In Chinese Medicine, we can apply the principles and diagnose whether an individual is Kidney Qi, Yin, Yang deficient, or a combination. Once the pattern of imbalance is identified, acupuncture, Chinese herbal medicine and appropriate food therapy can then be accurately prescribed.

Kidney Qi deficiency pattern will benefit from herbs that tonify Kidney Qi and foods that strengthens or boost Qi. Whereas if there is Kidney Yin deficiency, herbs and foods that support Yin should be used more proportionately.

The holistic nature of diagnosing and treating using Chinese Medicine means that every individual will have some variation in terms of therapeutic tools used, regardless of the diagnosis in modern medicine.

ii. Five Elements

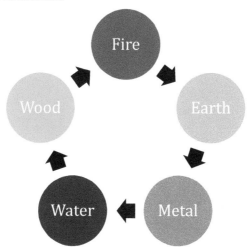

The Five Elements[5] has been taught around the world to TCM physicians for thousands of years. It explains the intricate relationship between each organ system and how the body is connected. Each element represents a pair of organs, a personality type, an emotion, a taste and seasonal change. It helps us understand how to best look after ourselves and our loved ones during different seasons, such as minimising physical exhaustion during Winter to conserve our Yang energy (our Yang keeps us warm in the cold). It also explains how eating foods seasonally aligns with nature and keeps our body in balance and health.

The purpose of introducing the Five Elements in this book is for me to show how it is applicable to our companion pets in our daily life. The full extensive explanation of Five Elements constitutes another book on its own. In this chapter, you will be guided through a concise summary in simple language. In the next diagram below I have included the respective organ systems.

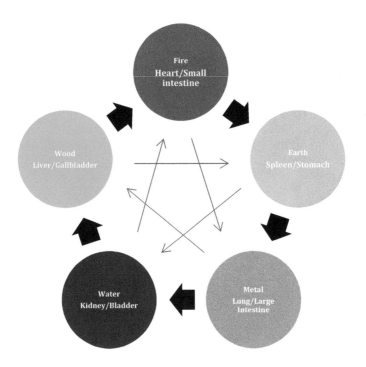

The bigger arrows on the circumference that connects the five elements forms the nourishing cycle, whereas the smaller arrows within forms the controlling cycle. The nourishing cycle shows how imbalances within an element can affect the next, and so forth. In simple words, one element nourishes the next, following the direction of the arrows. Therefore, accurate identification of the root element can help us focus and treat accordingly. For example, a weakened digestion (Spleen/Stomach) will eventually lead to chronic diarrhea (Large Intestine).

Note that "Spleen" in TCM refers to the entire digestive system. In this book I will often refer anything related to the gut as Spleen.

The controlling cycle (smaller arrows within) describes the restraining relationship between the elements, as the name already suggests. This relationship is important as it maintains balance and prevents an element to spin out of control. Harmony is key! In this circle within the five elements, Qi flows in an orderly fashion, yet with restrain.

Constitutions / Personalities

Each of us belong to a constitution (personality) that fits into either one or two elements. If you hover between two elements, one element will generally be predominant. The same applies for our domesticated dog, cat or horse. Contrasting constitutional differences in any environment is common and form a harmonious balance of yin and yang energy. This is true for most households with multiple pets, or even between family members. We are more likely to notice two dogs or cats with completely different constitutions. One might be fairly outgoing (Fire), the other could be more of a thinker and prefers to keep to him/herself (Metal/Water).

In a relationship between two individuals, we might say opposites attract. Children from the same family, who are all brought up the same way, will rarely belong to similar constitutions; there is always one that follows the rules and the other that breaks it or ignores it completely! This creates energetic balance and sustenance within our own ecosystem.

Fire

The Fire constitution is perhaps the most obvious out of all. In the veterinary context, this is an individual who is extremely outgoing, energetic and always within two feet from your face. He/she likes company and enjoys constant attention. They are friendly to everyone, dogs and humans alike. However, Fire dogs may also be the most challenging to train as they prefer to engage in the play more than to actually process thoughts. I say they tend to have selective hearing and a two second memory. Having said that, their actions may not always be rational!

The emotion associated with the Fire element is joy. Imbalances within the element can often result in anxiety or depression (Heart meridian). The nature of Fire is heat, so individuals belonging to this element may seek cold or prefers the cooler seasons. In another word, I call them "hot dogs". Due to the intolerance for heat in general, dogs living in countries with hot and dry summers may benefit from eating foods that are energetically cooling or neutral.

Examples of food: Turkey, Duck, Pork, Boar, Cod, Whiting, Rabbit, most leafy greens, apples, watermelon, pears.

Earth

Earth individuals are both friendly and laid-back. They are very easy going and extremely tolerant. They do enjoy touch and attention; however, they will also find time and space for rest. Earth constitutions are forgiving and do not tend to bear any grudges associated with negative experiences. Making friends is easy and second nature to them. Due to their eagerness to please others, training and discipline should not be difficult to achieve.

Worry is the associative emotion. Tendency to overthink and unnecessary worries can predispose them to stress related digestive upsets (Spleen and Stomach are the meridians associated with Earth). Within the controlling cycle (smaller inner arrows), a weakened Earth can also often be a result from an over controlling Wood. Digestion related deficiencies as well as Wood-Earth disharmonies are both common ailments amongst companion pets in the modern society.

This is where an integrated approach (using TCVM) can be successful when addressing digestive problems. If the Liver is involved in the disharmony, we tend to see stress related tummy upsets. (Discussed more in the next chapter – Wood). Bile vomiting with or without diarrhea may be random and inconsistent. Supplements that are supposedly good for the gut are only half as effective.

Wood

Dogs (and people) belonging to the Wood element generally tends to be assertive and dominant. They have great foresight and understanding of rules and boundaries. Wood dogs require minimal obedience training. They also have a mind of their own so when they set their sights on something, it can be difficult to change their minds. Having higher intelligence, they tend to lead the pack (including their human owners if they allow).

Their independence is usually obvious from the start, and may not crave for attention. Physical touch such as being patted, hugged or carried tends not to be their language of love.

The Liver helps to ground our emotions and also governs the smooth flow of Qi throughout our entire body. Anger is the associated emotion to the Wood element (Liver/Gallbladder). Emotional stress, long term medications, excessive parasitic prophylactic chemicals and inappropriate diets all make the Liver work harder to process and detoxify. In Chinese Medicine, this relates to Liver stagnancy. This can show up in a dog who may be irritable, or general dislike to other dogs. In the human world, think about people who makes irrational decisions after consumption of (too much) alcohol. They are likely to already have some degree of Liver stagnancy, possibly from work-life stress, and then made worse by the Liver's inability to process alcohol.

As discussed in the Earth element, internal digestive disorders caused by an overcontrolling Liver (stagnation) is a common manifestation. If the constitution of the dog is deemed to be Wood, then it becomes more relevant to apply both therapeutic and preventative principles when addressing the individual holistically.

Liver stagnancy produces internal heat which then rises, opening towards the eyes and ears, resulting in conjunctivitis and otitis. The Liver's paired organ is the Gallbladder. The Gallbladder meridian circles around the ears. The body attempts to expel excess Liver Heat via the paired Gallbladder system, which we so often see ear infections. As the sensory system that is linked to Wood belongs to the eye, Liver Heat often shows up as non-infectious conjunctivitis (redness around the eyes), typically worsening in Spring and Summer. In modern medicine, we simply refer these symptoms to as seasonal allergies.

Green and sour food will benefit the Wood element. For example, leafy greens, spirulina, chlorella, seaweeds, apple cider vinegar and fermented foods.

Water

Water in general is more yin in nature, as opposed to fire (yang). Dogs who belong to this element tend to be more introverted, and prefer to sit back and analyse a situation first than to jump straight into it. Being shy, Water dogs needs adequate time to settle in new environments, such as at the vet clinic or at social events. They also tend to cling on or hide behind owners, especially when the veterinarian attempts to do a physical examination. As with all introverts, social interactions with other dogs tend to be mentally draining and less enticing. They are most comfortable and interactive when at home.

The emotion associated with Water is fear. Excessive fear destabilises the Kidney/Bladder systems, represented clinically as lower back weakness or soreness, urinary incontinence and impotency. What this meant for individuals who belong to the Water element is to consider incorporating foods that benefits the Kidney such as bone broth, chicken eggs and bee pollen. Jing, or Essence, is what gives us life and longevity. Jing is stored in our Kidneys. Chronic fear and stress deplete the Kidney system.

Note that Kidney Jing is depleted at different rates between each individual, depending on factors like stress, illnesses or eating too much processed foods. As dogs belonging to the Water element tends to be a little more fearful, reducing stressors will better protect the Kidney.

Jing is divided into pre-natal and post-natal. Each of us gets a set amount of pre-natal Jing from our mothers, during development inside the womb. Post-natal Jing is derived directly from our diet. Imagine our pre-natal Jing as a bucket of water, each of our bucket starts off with varying amounts of water. At the bottom of the bucket is a small hole where water leaks at the same rate across every bucket; this is akin to time and the natural ageing process. Life is no longer possible once the bucket is empty. There is also an open tap at the top that fills the bucket; that is post-natal Jing (from food). How long can we preserve our Jing is largely influenced by dietary and lifestyles choices.

Food that benefits the Water element are eggs, kidney beans, seaweeds, spirulina, cinnamon.

Metal

Metal individuals are generally aloof. They appear confident and are not forthcoming. Organized, strong-headed, set in their ways and self-reliant are some of the words that come up with the Metal element. Dogs who belong to Metal are also extremely wise. They are generally tolerant of other dogs and rarely show signs of aggression. Grief is the emotion associated with Metal. Loss of a close companion may be difficult for them to accept and move on. The Lung and Large Intestine channels belong to the Metal element. In Chinese Medicine, Lung is in charge of distributing and fortifying our immunity (*Wei Qi, or defensive Qi*) against external pathogens. Imbalances in the Lung channel caused by emotional turmoil can disrupt our Wei Qi and allow pathogens to invade and cause illnesses. Pathogens may refer to infectious causes such as bacteria and viruses, or TCM pathogens such as Wind, Cold, Heat, Dryness and Dampness. For example, a Wind invasion with Cold, can cause sudden nasal congestion with headaches. Humans or dogs who experience severe grief may subsequently succumb to some form of illnesses.

The biggest enemy of Lung is dryness. This is where moistening foods, or foods that produce bodily fluids are extremely beneficial. This keeps the element in check, and thus smooth flow of Qi and normal immune function.

	Fire	Earth	Metal	Water	Wood
Organ	Heart	Digestion	Lung	Kidney	Liver
Emotion	Joy	Worry	Grief	Fear	Anger
Personality trait	Happy-go-lucky	Friendly, eager to please	Aloof, quiet, confident	Introverted	Dominant, smart
Sensory	Tongue	Mouth	Nose	Ears	Eyes
Flavour	Bitter	Sweet	Pungent	Salty	Sour
Season	Summer	Late Summer	Autumn	Winter	Spring

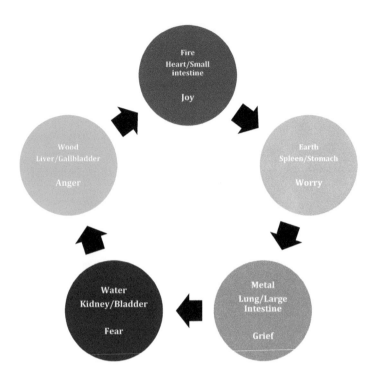

Can you figure out which element you or your dog belongs to?

iii.   Deciphering tongues and pulse quality

Tongue and pulse reading remain one of most crucial and valuable diagnostic tools in Chinese Medicine. Veterinarians around the world who practice TCVM cannot perform a complete assessment without looking at their patients' tongues and palpation of femoral pulses. This is because Chinese Medicine treats the root imbalances. Individual's imbalances are often referred to as "pattern diagnosis". A specific pattern of imbalance needs to be identified before tools can be implemented to correct it. We nourish one's deficiencies, and get rid of one's excesses (*Heat, Cold, Damp, Phlegm, Stagnation*). Acupuncture, Chinese herbology and food therapy are tools of Chinese Medicine.

When assessing the tongue, the colour, moisture, coating, shape and size are taken into consideration. These traits of the tongue simply reflect the health and balance of internal organs. To an untrained eye, the simplest way is to ascertain the colour of your dog's tongue. Ask yourself, is the tongue pink, pale, red or lavender in colour? If the tongue has a pale complexion, there is lack of Qi; we are staring at a deficient individual. Sufficient Qi is necessarily to circulate blood, which then gives the tongue a more robust and vibrant colour. A lavender or purple tinge indicates stagnation; which could relate to musculoskeletal pain, or internal stress. Excess body heat or deficiency in Yin (false heat) will reflect a dark pink or red tongue. This colour of the tongue is most obvious when you compare it against the colour of the gums, by lifting either side of the upper lip.

Pink tongues; healthy

Pale pink; indicating Qi deficiencies

Dark red tongues; indicating excess Heat or Yin Deficiencies

Lavender tongues; indicating excess Cold or Stagnation

<u>Palpating the femoral pulses</u>

Pulse reading is a skill that is taught in theory yet can only be learnt via experience. TCM physicians read human pulses via the radial artery on the thumb side of the wrist. TCVM practitioners read dog and cat pulses via the femoral artery, on the inner aspect of the thighs. The common carotid artery (neck region) is palpated in horses, and the ventral tail artery in cows. The rate, depth and size of the pulse provides the practitioner more detailed information of the individual's imbalances. A slow and deep pulse generally suggests a deficient state whereas a superficial or forceful pulse indicates the presence of excesses (heat, false heat, stagnation).

Tongue reading, palpation of pulses together with a full medical history and physical examination will help us form a "pattern diagnosis". This is then used to determine the optimal course of treatment using acupuncture, herbal medicine and food therapy – to simply bring the body back into balance.

Here is an illustration.

9 years old "Molly" is a Terrier mixed breed who presented for kidney failure. Her tongue is pale pink with deep and weak pulses. She sleeps most of the day and shows little interest in activities such as play or going for a walk. Drinking habits remained normal. TCVM pattern diagnosis for Molly is *Kidney Qi Deficiency*.

10 years old "Jack" is a Retriever mixed breed who also presented for kidney failure. He had a dark red-looking tongue, with thin and rapid pulses. He seemed to feel hot all the time, with excessive panting even when the air-conditioning is switched on. His drinking has also increased by 30% and urinating more throughout the day and night. Jacko has trouble sleeping through the night and often wakes up multiple times to drink or urinate. Energy remains good

and looks forward to daily walks. Jack's TCVM pattern diagnosis is *Kidney Yin Deficiency*.

You may recall the four essential substances (Qi, Blood, Yin and Yang) in the earlier chapters. Qi deficiency will often reflect a paler pink tongue, with deep pulses as there is little "pressure" to move Blood towards the tongue to give its normal rosy pink color. Without sufficient Qi, circulation is poor which then translate to lethargy and fatigue. This explains Molly's TCVM pattern diagnosis. As she is mainly Qi deficient, the physician may prescribe acupuncture points and herbs that strengthen Kidney Qi.

Yin, on the other hand, is what keeps us cool, maintains bodily fluids and helps with grounding, allowing us to have normal sleep cycles through the night (night = yin, day = yang). Yin deficiency is also known as "false heat", due to a relatively excess Yang in the body. This causes the tongue to be a darker shade of red than usual. Without adequate Yin to ground our thoughts, dogs may be restless, and find it difficult to have restful nights.

The above illustration explains the very fundamentals of Traditional Chinese Veterinary Medicine and how treatments tend to differ between individuals, even with the same disease.

6. THERMAL PROPERTIES OF FOOD

Meat, grains, vegetables and herbs all have other properties that go beyond its flavor, taste and nutritional value. We can simply group them together based on whether they are cooling, neutral or warming. In other words, warming foods heat the body up and cooling foods do the opposite. For example, chilies and ginger are both considered energetically hot. Think about what happens when you eat them. Watermelon, pears and celery are all energetically cold, great to cool off excess body heat especially during the warmer seasons.

How does this apply to dogs, who are mostly carnivorous, and requires little fruit and vegetables, let alone spices? Following eastern traditions and philosophies dating back a few thousand years, meat proteins have also been observed to have similar thermal properties[6]. Food has always been a fundamental aspect of Chinese medicine, where early physicians would diagnose a patient's imbalances and write up prescriptions of herbal medicines and recommend specific foods to eat or avoid entirely. Even before plants were identified and known to have medicinal value, eating appropriate foods (in moderation) is preventive medicine on its own. Afterall, many herbs we know now were plants in the wild that had been tasted and tested, whether intentionally or not.

Innate thermal properties of food can also change depending on the cooking or processing method. For instance, steamed sweet potato has a neutral energy. It becomes much warmer when they are fried or baked into sweet potato chips. Chicken is warming on its own, and becomes much hotter when roasted or fried. Chicken soup or broth is used in many cultures for nourishing the gut and recovery postillness. The same chicken, when roasted or fried, is hugely avoided for this purpose due to its extreme heaty nature.

Thermal energy of meat can also differ depending on the animal's predominant diet throughout its life. Generally speaking, beef is a neutral protein, assuming they ate mostly grass and other plant materials. Intensively farmed beef can have a very different diet, such as grain-finished, meaning the cattle spends their last 10-15% of their lives away from a solely grass diet. This may be due to a number of factors including fulfilling consumers' demands, as well as considering the profitability and sustainability of modern farming methods. Depending on where your local butcher sources their beef from, the thermal energy of beef can range between neutral to warm.

Understanding and applying the thermal values of meat proteins to your dog's diet can have a huge impact in the longer term. You might ask, wouldn't it be fine to feed my dog a variation of meat proteins? It is ideal to always have variety however our perspectives may change when we start to appreciate individual differences between dogs, even within the same breed. Like humans, some dogs feel the heat more, whereas others may feel the cold easily. A good proportion of the population will have neither obvious heat or cool seeking behavior. The hot dogs pant easily, and tend to prefer laying on cold tiles or flooring. They are also intolerant of heat and may tire easily. Chilly dogs tend to love sun baking, such as following the sunny spots throughout the day.

Striving for balance is key. The general rule is that hot individuals will thrive with more cooling foods, and vice versa for chilly individuals. Note that I used the word 'balance', which is the fundamental principle in Chinese Medicine. Any extremes in the hot or cold spectrum, for prolonged periods of time without re-evaluating the changing needs of an individual, will result in imbalances. Imbalances that aren't resolved may then lead to a diseased state later. For instance, most cooling foods have Yin-nourishing properties, but little Qi tonifying value (some foods have multiple properties; will be discussèd later). The gut in all warm-blooded mammals can only function efficiently when it is nourished appropriately. Wholesome foods are a must, but importantly foods that can supply Qi, to generate sufficient post-natal Jing for health. For an individual that feels the heat, eating more cooling foods will certainly offset the heat, however eating only cold foods for long periods may result in unwanted adverse consequences in other aspects of health.

Common animal proteins and their thermal energy:

Cold: Duck, Rabbit, Turkey, Mussels, Shark, Frog, White Bait, Cod

Neutral: Pork, Beef (grass fed), Sardine, Tuna, Mackerel, Quail, Egg

Warm: Chicken, Salmon, Beef (grain fed)

Hot: Lamb, Kangaroo, Goat, Emu, Camel, Horse, Venison

7. SEVEN SPECIAL PROPERTIES OF FOOD

Besides classifying foods into their thermal energies, each food also contains other special properties. Qi, Blood, Yin or Yang tonifying, Damp draining, Phlegm resolving and Stagnation moving are the seven special properties. Deficiencies are generally straightforward; if one is Qi deficient, then Qi tonifying foods will be beneficial. If there is a combination of deficiencies, then feed a variety of foods from both categories.

Damp, Phlegm and Stagnation are complex concepts in TCM and are defined by much broader meanings than the definition of the word itself. They are considered excess conditions that disrupts our normal flow of Qi, affecting both physical and emotional health. "Food can be your slowest form of poison, or can be your best medicine." Certain foods, if eaten in excess, are considered unhealthy as they may put extra stress on your digestion. In Chinese Medicine, we refer to these categories of food as Damp engendering.

i. Damp draining

Dampness in Chinese Medicine is considered a pathogen, along with others such as Wind, Cold, Heat and Dryness. I have capitalized each pathogenic factor as they have a much broader meaning in TCM. From each meaning of the word itself we can quickly realize why they are referred to as pathogens; too much of either can disturb homeostasis and lead to illnesses.

For those who are familiar or have had experiences with Chinese Medicine, be it personally or with an integrative TCVM veterinarian, Damp is one of the most commonly used term to describe a chronic condition that the body struggles to recover from. When the body harbours excess Damp, the normal flow of Qi is impaired. Circulation becomes poor, healing is suboptimal and overall energy will be diminished, causing lethargy. Clinical symptoms generally depend on which organ system is affected. For example, recurring urinary tract infections is due to Damp Heat in the Bladder, frequent loose stools with mucous is due to Dampness in the Spleen element (digestion), osteoarthritis that shows more stiffness than pain has Damp within the joints. External ear infections, yeast overgrowth in groin regions and paws are reflections of Damp Heat within the Liver system. In many of such instances, herbal medicine and foods that drain Damp can be very successful in resolving recurring symptoms or reducing reliance on medications.

To learn about Damp-draining foods we must first realize what foods engender Damp - too much raw foods, food containing refined sugars, highly processed foods such as dry pet diets, dairy products like cheese, and fried or greasy foods. Essentially these foods make the Spleen work harder and consume more Qi, which eventually weakens and slows down its normal functions of transforming food into useful energy. When the Spleen works at suboptimal capacity for prolonged periods, Dampness accumulates, resulting in symptoms such as bloating, increased flatulence, loose stools often with a mucous coating and sometimes poorer appetite.

There are many foods that have Damp-draining properties, such as apple cider vinegar, pumpkin, kidney beans, mackerel, celery, alfalfa, barley and garlic. All of the foods mentioned are easily accessible, and safe for dogs to consume. The only caution for garlic is that it must not exceed 5% of their daily diet – mainly due to is extremely hot nature. The same applies for humans, eating the equivalent percentage of garlic in our diet will most certainly induce diarrhea. However, a small amount used in cooking, or eaten raw, is highly beneficial. I have also applied this technique with food therapy in my veterinary patients, especially those with a stubborn constitution.

Foods rarely have just one single property. Garlic can also help move stagnation, open up sinuses and empty bowels. Apple cider vinegar benefits the Liver in the detoxification process, enhance Qi flow, digestion and reducing sluggishness (Damp). Pumpkin nourishes the gut (Spleen Qi) and helps with both diarrhea and constipation, owing to the presence of soluble and insoluble fibre.

ii.   Phlegm

The concept of Phlegm and Dampness in TCM can be rather similar, depending on the context of the patient. Both pathogens arise from a dysfunction in fluid metabolism, which is govern by the digestive system (Spleen). The basic understanding of phlegm is something that is sticky and hard to move, which sounds like Damp! Phlegm can either be manifested as a physical symptom; such as in respiratory tract infections and lipomas (fatty lumps under the skin), or as an intangible external expression of internal imbalances.

Phlegm in the head can cause obstruction to the normal flow of Qi, resulting in headaches or seizures. Phlegm can also be combined with pathogenic Heat/Fire and cause significant fogging of the Heart element which leads to behavioral issues, typically with non-aggressive individuals seemingly making irrational decisions.

Some of the common foods that can transform Phlegm are almonds, pears, apples, radish, garlic, seaweed, thyme, peppermint and ginger. Seaweed or kelp is a common addition to our dogs' meals due to its beneficial properties on oral hygiene, so most pet owners may already be fairly aware of its use. Seaweed also contains iodine to support normal thyroid function, plus many other essential trace vitamins and minerals in small quantities to help bolster the nutritional profile of a home-made diet. Seaweeds and other microalgae will be discussed more in depth under the *Superfoods* chapter.

Almonds are also known for its rich sources of magnesium, vitamin E and dietary fibre. A medium-sized dog between 15 to 25kg will only require about 4-5 almonds per day. The most common application for this would be dogs with lipomas. We must always remember to consider the dog's basic diet. For instance, adding almonds to a predominantly highly processed diet (which generates Damp/Phlegm) tends to have a minimal influence.

iii. Stagnation

Stagnation is simply referred to as traffic jams. Imagine Qi and Blood flowing through our meridians, into each organ systems, nourishing every cell constantly for growth and repair. Meridians are like roads that connect our body together. A traffic jam in any part of the meridian pathways may be mild and easily resolved, or can be significant and harder to move.

Physical or emotional stress stagnates (Liver) Qi. Physical stressors could be caused by medications, chemicals, inappropriate diets and excessive strenuous exercises. Emotional stress may stem from anxiety, rehoming and constitutional differences, making some dogs more sensitive and susceptible.

Where there is pain in the body, there is stagnation. Qi stagnation in the muscles or joints often causes stiffness and a dull aching sore. Massages, physical touch and warmth alleviates pain. Blood stagnation might be more acute, such as sprains or traumatic injuries, and typically induces a sharp focal pain. Touch exacerbates pain. Dogs with severe hip or elbow dysplasia may often have a combination of Qi and Blood Stagnation due to incongruent joints causing secondary muscular compensation and dysfunction.

Regardless of the type of stagnation, dogs often have a tongue that reflects a lavender tinge. The intensity of the lavender color as well as moisture and any coating on the tongue, depends on any other underlying deficiencies or excesses. Dogs who are deficient in Qi and dealing with chronic osteoarthritis may show a pale lavender colored tongue. Acute injuries will often present with a darker lavender tinged tongue.

Understanding which form of stagnation can be very helpful in allowing us to choose an appropriate combination of foods. Both chicken and lamb have stagnation moving properties. Chicken resolve stagnation by tonifying and moving Qi. Lamb can nourish Blood, raise the body's Yang energy and increase circulation. Other commonly used foods include venison, crab, mustard greens, dill seeds, watercress, coriander, ginger, turmeric, garlic, apple cider vinegar and parsley. These foods have a pungent flavour, which are also used to help treat disorders in specific channels.

iv.   Qi, Blood, Yin and Yang tonifying

Foods that harbour these four properties are primarily used to support deficiencies. Qi and Blood tonifying foods improve circulation and help increase the body's natural healing capacity. Examples of food are chicken, beef, sardines, eggs, sweet potato and livers. Individuals with these deficiencies have tongues that are pale in colour and weak femoral pulses. They may also have sluggish energy, haircoat that sheds easily and a generally poorer immunity that makes them susceptible to repetitive health issues. A dog with Qi deficiency in the Spleen may have chronic diarrhea, a thin body condition and feels the cold easily. A dog with Qi deficiency in the

Lung may present with bronchitis, recurrent upper respiratory tract infections or laryngeal paralysis.

Food with Yin energy usually have cooling and moistening effects, increasing the production of bodily fluids. Examples are duck, rabbit, pork, honey, mussels, spinach and peas. Deficiency in Yin is a specific pattern of imbalance that can represent a myriad of diseases. Common ones include Cushing's disease, kidney disease, heart failure and allergic skin disease where individuals always seemed hot and thirsty. There may also be unexplained panting, especially at night. This is attributed to "false heat", also referred as Yin deficiency. Imagine our body has an in-built air conditioning system and Yin is the gas within. Without adequate gas, the air-conditioner can only produce un-cooled air, creating a sense of false heat over time. When Yin-nourishing foods are consumed, the body is able to generate and retain bodily fluids to help maintain thermostatic control.

On the other hand, food that strengthen and raise the body's Yang energy are warming. Examples are lamb, venison, cinnamon, ginger, garlic, rosemary and thyme. Yang deficiency is much less common and it is usually not a good sign. It reflects the later stages when Qi is almost completely exhausted due to age or chronic illnesses. Dogs who are Yang deficient often lose the sparkle in their eyes and are cold to touch. Loose watery diarrhea without odour and large volumes of clear urine are common symptoms. Yang tonifying foods can be very heating, so caution with feeding too much of them to dogs who may be Yin deficient. It is easy to think about how you feel when ginger, garlic or cinnamon is consumed – the heat generated from within raises your core body temperature.

Noting the different properties of animal proteins, vegetables, herbs, fruits and spices, it is important to eat a variety of food in a healthy individual. This creates energetic homeostasis over time. For example, rotating through lamb (warm), duck (cool) and perhaps beef (neutral) will make sense over a combination of lamb and venison (both warm).

More functional foods in their respective categories are listed under *Food Energetics – Quick Reference Guide* chapter at the end of the book.

8. HEALING WITH WHOLESOME FOODS

Eating wholesome foods, or foods that are minimally processed, significantly reduces the likelihood of disease. Besides retaining their nutritive value as a whole, they also harbor an abundance of Qi which is then transformed into other forms of energy upon digestion. Qi is neither created nor destroyed, it is merely transformed. When dealing with an illness, our body draws from our energy reserve (known as Yuan Qi or Source Qi, stored in the Kidney system). Overdrawing without adequately replenishing it leads to a prolonged course of disease. Discussed in the Water section of the Five Element Theory, our post-natal Jing (essence) is derived directly from real foods.

Highly processed foods contain carcinogens, which is linked to various types of cancers if eaten in excess, in both human and dogs alike. What are whole foods? They refer to unrefined grains, beans, legumes, nuts, seeds, fruits and vegetables. Some examples are wheat, quinoa, rolled oats, lentils, kidney beans, sunflower seeds, linseeds, pumpkin seeds, fruits and vegetables in their unaltered forms.

While dogs are predominantly meat eaters, they are also fairly efficient at digesting any of the above foods, provided they are "partially digested" or cooked. This is especially true for certain common foods we feed our dogs, such as green leafy vegetables, carrots, pumpkin and sweet potato. In the ancestral diet, the only way they have the opportunity to ingest any grains, seeds, vegetable and fruit material is via the gut contents of a smaller mammal. Within the gut contents are also digestive enzymes that have already broken down the hard cellular walls of plant material, seeds and grains – allowing them to be digestible.

i.   Raw or cooked?

Is raw or cooked better for dogs? It depends. Just as it is true for humans and other living mammals, no one-size-fits-all diet exists. There are guidelines and standards that help shape our nutritional requirements. However, within those guidelines there is also flexibility to suit individual needs.

Dogs who may be recovering from an illness, have a chronic condition such as kidney failure, natural old age or fighting cancers have some degree of deficiency. Cooked diets may be better suited as they are easier to digest. In these circumstances we want to supply good Qi directly to the body without overworking the Spleen. Supposed your dog had to be hospitalized and is recovering from a crisis of some sort. Veterinary staff will typically feed dogs cooked chicken breast (owing to its accessibility, affordability and low in fat) in an attempt to regain appetite which is also an indicator of improving vitality. The notion of using something fresh, wholesome and cooked is almost instinctual and human nature, as we want to optimize recovery in ill patients. Dogs are then often sent home and told to feed similar bland diets using cooked meats with or without a carbohydrate source, for continued recovery in the short term.

Raw diets on the other hand would ideally be best for dogs who are young and healthy otherwise, or have conditions relating to excess Heat. In Chinese Medicine, raw foods consume more Qi in the process of digestion, possibly leaving the individual more tired after. Excessive raw foods also engender Damp, owing to an overworked Spleen system. Our Spleen system (digestion) is analogous to a cooking pot simmering on low heat. Any significant deviation from the normal simmering temperature (approximately 37 degree Celsius) may cause unwanted issues such as gastric reflux, vomiting, bloating, indigestion or diarrhea. In fact, these are some of the most common reasons dogs do better onto cooked meals, as opposed to raw or other forms of processed foods. As the famous saying goes, "the root of all disease stems from the gut."

Dogs who are raw fed, compared to dogs on a cooked diet will not have the same gut microbiome diversity. This is also true for dogs who are fed a predominantly processed (dry kibble) diet. Dogs who are used to eating raw meats can generally tolerate raw bones, which are a great source of dietary calcium and plays a key part in maintaining dental hygiene. One of the challenges of a cooked diet is to also fulfil the needs for dental hygiene without raw meaty bones. Calcium is easily supplemented via eggshells, coral calcium powders or even calcium tablets. Cooked bones should never be fed to dogs due to the risk of splintering plus the fact that they are completely indigestible.

Dogs who are on a cooked diet can still be fed raw bones, mainly to keep teeth clean. This is also true for deficient dogs, as long as they are up for a good chew. In TCVM and holistic medicine, the ultimate goal is balance. Balance is looking at the overall diet over a period of time, considering one individual's needs, rather than being assessed on a per day basis. A deficient dog getting one raw bone every so often is likely to enjoy much longer-term benefits in terms of oral health, as opposed to having none at all.

The jaws of canids are not designed to chew food as much as humans do, so optimal digestion of vegetables can only happen if they are either steamed or blitzed up into a pulp. This can also greatly reduce the chances of rejection from dogs with a finicky appetite. Carrots are one of the most common vegetables some pet owners feed their dogs, in various forms – whole, chopped up, pre-cut frozen cubes, grated, blitzed or cooked. Being a root vegetable, canids lack specific enzymes that can break down the tough outer wall of raw carrots. Increasing the surface area will improve the chances of it being absorbed better. For example, grated carrots are digested quicker as opposed to large cubes. This is most evident when we notice bright orange bits of undigested carrots in our dogs' stools, especially when fed whole. The same applies to corn kernels (without the cob), which are by and large impossible to digest.

9. SUPERFOODS

Superfoods are natural supplements or foods used to boost the nutritive value of any diet. With the rise in intensive farming systems, crops are grown on soil that are depleted of minerals quicker than it can replenish. Perhaps the accumulation of toxic chemicals in our environment and the increased affordability of processed foods have led to multiple deficiencies in our modern diets as a whole. In the past decade we have seen a steady trend of pet owners reaching for natural fresh diets as opposed to dry processed diets. It is also not surprising to see many of us becoming more proactive in preventative health, especially with younger dogs seemingly becoming more susceptible to skin allergies, inflammatory bowel issues as well as cancers.

The definition of superfoods can be applied broadly. However, I have narrowed them down to the list below for the purpose of the veterinary context. These are also foods which I commonly incorporate as part of an integrative nutrition consultation and TCVM food therapy for specific individual's requirements.

➢ Spirulina/Chlorella (micro-algae)
➢ Seaweed (macro-algae)
➢ Bone broth
➢ Eggs
➢ Bee pollen
➢ Bovine colostrum
➢ Mushrooms
➢ Fermented foods
➢ Kidney beans

➤ Turmeric

i. Spirulina/Chlorella

The micro-algae are known for their impressive and condensed nutrient profiles; a natural source of protein, essential fatty acids, provitamin A and numerous trace minerals such as zinc, iron, magnesium. They are also sometimes known as "Super Greens" – which contains the micro-algae and other complementary supplements. Widely available from most health food stores and chemists, remember to make sure the products are reliable and have gone through a third-party testing for quality control. Products targeted at the human market may also contain grape seed or blackcurrant extracts, which are highly toxic to both dogs and cats – so choose those without. A safe option is to get Spirulina or Chlorella just on its own.

The vitamins and trace minerals in almost all dry diets are artificial and synthetically added during production – mainly to meet AAFCO nutritional standards and labelling requirements. Bioavailability and absorption of synthetic vitamins and minerals to the canine gut is both variable and questionable. Natural sources of vitamins and minerals in wholesome foods are impossible to remain viable when exposed to high temperatures and drying methods. Adding either spirulina or chlorella to any diets will therefore significantly boost its nutritional value. There are some minor but important differences between spirulina and chlorella when it comes to applying them for specific health conditions.

Spirulina

Spirulina contains an extraordinary amount of protein, GLA fatty acids[7], beta carotene and chlorophyll, which are all used to tackle inflammatory conditions. It can also reduce blood glucose, cholesterol and blood pressure. The high protein in spirulina is especially beneficial for individuals who have trouble digesting normal amounts of animal protein, such as those with pancreatitis or inflammatory bowel disease. Dogs presenting with severe liver stagnancy (inability to perform routine detoxification process) from chronic diseases and medications will greatly benefit from supplementation. Spirulina is also proven to boost the gut microbiome, owing to its microbial-modulating activities when supplemented together with probiotics. This presents as a new strategy in prevention of gut dysbiosis[8] (common cause of food intolerances and chronic diarrhea).

Spirulina's blue-green color comes from a pigment-protein complex called phycocyanin which increases the body's resistance to diseases by promoting blood cell regeneration and improving function of the lymphatic system. Also used widely in anti-cancer therapies, phycocyanin can block tumor cell cycles[9], making it a must-have in diets when treating cancers.

*GLA = gamma linolenic acid

Chlorella

The nutritional value of chlorella is similar to that of spirulina, however it has more fatty acids and about twice the amount of chlorophyll. Structurally, it has an outer cell wall which has the ability to bind up heavy metals and toxins, including carcinogens, and carry them out of the body. Chlorella also contains Chlorella Growth Factor (CGF) within its DNA. CGF has this unique ability to promote growth, healing and repair[10]; widely studied in humans with degenerative diseases or stunted growth from various reasons. This can potentially be applied widely across the veterinary context as a powerful adjunct therapy, mostly for individuals presenting with deficiencies. Chlorella does not contain the pigment phycocyanin, found in spirulina, and therefore do not possess the anti-cancer properties.

In Chinese Medicine food therapy, micro-algae are considered Jing (essence) tonics. They also tonify Qi and Blood. They enter the Liver, Spleen and Kidney systems, resolving Qi stagnation (oxidative stress) and increase longevity by bolstering our reserves of Jing. The actions of spirulina and chlorella are considered to be cooling, tonifying and cleansing (detoxifying).

The taste is generally well accepted by dogs (and cats). In my experience, the dosage I have found effective is a quarter of a teaspoon powder added to a meal, for every 10-15kg bodyweight. They can be given once or twice daily, depending on the number of meals. Healthy dogs may only require such addition a few times each week. Individuals on long term medications, such as corticosteroids, immunosuppressants and antibiotics, may benefit from consistent supplementation. Both spirulina and chlorella are cooling and have strong cleansing properties so care must be exercised for individuals who exhibits more deficient signs – introverted, quiet, tendency to have loose stools, indigestion, poor appetite, lackluster hair coat, warmth seeking habits or cool extremities (ears, paws and lower back).

To summarise the benefits of micro-algae:
- Anti-oxidative
- Anti-inflammatory
- Anti-cancer (spirulina only)
- Liver protective
- Source of iodine to support healthy thyroid function
- Aids detoxification processes
- Improve lymphatic circulation and drainage

- Promote regeneration of healthy blood cells

Caution: Micro-algae and seaweeds should be avoided in individuals with an overactive thyroid (hyperthyroidism; more common in elderly cats) due to their higher iodine content. Instead, they should ideally be fed an iodine restrictive diet. Dogs, as opposed to cats, are more susceptible to having an underactive thyroid (hypothyroidism). This means there is a wider safety margin when considering using Spirulina or Chlorella in dogs.

Conditions indicated for:

- Hypothyroidism
- Cancers
- Skin allergies
- Kidney insufficiency/failure
- Cushing's syndrome
- Autoimmune diseases

ii. Seaweeds

There are around 10,000 species of seaweed around the world, and can be categorized into red, brown and green seaweeds. The largest group belongs to the red seaweeds, containing around 6500 species. Dulse is a type of red seaweed that is a popular snack in Scotland and Ireland. Nori, also a type of red seaweed, is used commonly in Japanese cuisine to make sushi. Brown seaweeds have around 1800 species, including *Ascophyllum nodosum* and kelp. *Ascophyllum nodosum* is one of the most widely studied[11] seaweed and also commonly sold as dietary supplements. Sustainable harvesting methods have made *Ascophyllum nodosum* a more viable option to meet increasing consumer demands. Kelp, on the other hand, are much larger in size and grows in deep ocean waters where they form ecosystems in their own right. These kelp forests are typically protected and can only be harvested after they have been washed up on the shoreline. One example is Bull Kelp, found in Tasmania.

Nutritionally, seaweeds are a rich source of iodine and fibre, with an abundance of vitamins (A, C, E) and trace minerals. Similar to the micro-algae, iodine is essential for a healthy thyroid function. The hormones (Triiodothyronine T3, Tetraiodothyronine T4 and Calcitonin) produced by the thyroid gland helps regulate our body's metabolism by transforming food into energy. Together with the trace minerals in seaweeds they help optimise absorption of other nutrients. Seaweeds also aid the liver's natural detoxification process, owing to the presence of chlorophyll and phytopigments.

In TCVM food therapy, seaweeds are energetically cooling, meaning they are used for clearing conditions relating to excess Heat; similar to the microalgae. They also help transform phlegm and soften hard masses; such as lipomas and tumors. In fact, a particular specie of kelp called *Laminaria japonica*[12] (*Hai Zao*) is often used in Chinese veterinary herbology to assist in the process of softening hard masses and shrink tumours.

As our soils become more deficient with modern intensive agricultural methods, foods grown in them today contain may not contain the same nutritional density. Profound mineral deficiencies are then exacerbated by eating or feeding more processed foods. Seaweeds and the microalgae can supplement the diverse deficiencies, especially trace minerals. Remember that synthetic minerals and vitamins added to any processed foods does not necessarily guarantee their bioavailability. The term 'processed foods' refer to any other type of edible food products other than wholefoods in their natural shape and form. In the context of our companion animals, it refers to dry, canned, freeze-dried and air-dried diets.

Conditions indicated for:

- o Hypothyroidism
- o Cushing's syndrome
- o Tumours; specifically for nodules or space occupying masses

iii. **Bone broth**

Bone broth is one of the superfoods that can be used on its own to provide excellent short-termed nutrition. This is especially true for deficient or sick individuals who may not have their usual appetite. Self-made broth is an option, however there are also good quality commercially prepared options available. I typically use a full chicken carcass, roughly chopped up, and fill the crockpot with water just enough to cover the highest point of the carcass. Carrots, corn, cabbages and a few cloves of garlic are some of the other foods I personally add to boost its flavor and nutritional value. Bring to a boil and then simmer on the lowest heat for at least 90 minutes or longer.

Other types of bones you would choose are those with the cartilaginous bits, such joints, ribs and spinal bones of cows, sheep or pigs. The broth making process extracts abundance of glucosamine and chondroitin, the building blocks for healthy joints, which are helpful for conditions such as osteoarthritis, tendon or ligament injuries and spinal diseases (eg. intervertebral disc disease). Illnesses, antibiotic use or recovery from general anesthesia are some of the other scenarios where pre-made broth may come in extremely handy to give your furry companion a much-needed boost.

Bone broth nourishes *Spleen Qi* and replenishes *Kidney Jing*. Being a liquid, it is easily absorbed without having the digestive system to work hard at all. Also used commonly as a form of complementary nutrition for many healthy dogs, the broth can be kept refrigerated then fed as jelly blocks, or kept frozen for use later. An excellent meal topper.

Conditions indicated for:

- Inflammatory bowel disease
- Pancreatitis
- Osteoarthritis
- General ageing

iv.   Eggs

The humble egg has the range of vitamins and minerals that often complements what a predominantly meat-based diet may lack. Choline, Vitamin D, Vitamin B12, Folate, Lutein and Zeaxanthin are the main nutrients that comes to mind.

Choline is an essential nutrient that is vital for the body to produce certain phospholipids, which are used to synthesize cell membranes in all aspects of the body. The dog's (and human's) liver can produce some choline. However, deficiencies can develop over time if not supplemented in the diet. Ability to synthesize cell membranes relate to healthy heart function, muscle, liver, brain and the nervous system. Deficiencies may often be subtle and reflect later on in life with issues like heart disease and premature cognitive decline. Livers and red meats are amongst other foods that also contain choline.

Egg is a potent *Jing* tonic. The egg white has more *yin* energy whereas the egg yolk is *yang* on its own. Eaten as a whole it becomes energetically neutral. Individuals who are deficient in *Jing* will benefit from having eggs included regularly in their diet. Patterns of

Jing deficiency will present with congenital growth defects, hips or elbow dysplasia, fear based behavioral issues as well as dogs who were neutered prematurely.

For healthy otherwise individuals, having one to two eggs per week is adequate. The shell is an excellent natural source of calcium, so adding it (crushed up) to food increases the value of the meal and reduces wastage. Can a dog have an egg daily? Absolutely. They can either be fed raw or boiled. Always remember to strive for balance, feed in moderation according to your dog's needs.

Conditions indicated for:

- o Congenital growth disorders
- o Behavioural issues (fear based) in puppies
- o Heart diseases
- o Liver disease
- o Cushing's syndrome
- o Addison's disease
- o Diabetes mellitus

v. Bee Pollen

Bee pollen, as the name suggests, is essentially pollen collected from flowering plants. If you look closely enough at bees, you may sometimes notice a yellow to orange bulb on their hind legs. They are called the pollen baskets, where pollen is stored prior returning to the hive. Within the hive, flightless bees process the pollen by adding saliva and covering it with a layer of wax. At this stage, the substance is called bee bread which is fermented anaerobically. Bee bread is the basic source of protein for the bee colony. Worker bees also use bee bread to make royal jelly, another excellent superfood!

Bee pollen is recognized for both its nutritional and valuable medicinal benefits. Medical applications include proven local analgesia and improving the healing process of burn wounds[13]. As a dietary supplement, it has strong anti-inflammatory properties, anti-fungal, anti-microbial, anti-viral, liver protective and anti-cancer via immunomodulation[14]. This is owing to its richness in biologically active substances like protein, amino acids, essential fatty acids, enzymes, carbohydrates, coenzymes and vitamins. According to TCVM food therapy principles, it tonifies *Qi* and *Blood*, nourishes *Jing*. Like any other dietary supplements, bee pollen should not be taken in large amounts over a long period of time. It should instead be used in moderation and to complement a balanced diet.

Conditions indicated for:

- o Autoimmune diseases
- o Cancers
- o Inflammatory bowel diseases

vi. Bovine Colostrum

A gentle and important *Jing* tonic, colostrum is a substance produced by mothers only in the first few hours to days of birth. It contains an abundance of antibodies, enzymes and essential nutrients designed to optimize the offspring's immune system and guide their gut microbiome in the best direction. Bovine colostrum is available on the shelves in most human health food stores, either in a powder or tablet form. Always read the product labels to determine the strength of colostrum per serve.

Bovine colostrum has proven therapeutic effects on range of digestion associated issues such as non-steroidal inflammatory drug

(NSAIDs) induced gut ulcers, inflammatory bowel disease as well as chemotherapy induced mucositis[15]. Too many dogs are on long term NSAIDs for osteoarthritis, chronic ligament injuries as well as peri-operatively for orthopaedic procedures. A good proportion of these dogs will develop mild to moderate reactions such as bile vomiting or diarrhea. Subclinical gastrointestinal erosions[16] are common in these circumstances, which suggests that dogs with pre-existing gut issues must exercise caution when using any NSAIDs. If NSAIDs is unavoidable for many reasons including maintenance of life quality, then a fresh diet with appropriate supplements that protect the gut should be instilled.

Inflammatory or irritable bowel disease is a condition relating to individuals with a chronically inflamed gut and may have gastric reflux and/or loose stools frequently. Dietary choices are restrictive, often limiting to one single protein. It is also not uncommon for these dogs to still experience waxing and waning bouts of poor digestion, likely to due to an underlying dysbiosis. Dysbiosis refers to the disharmony within the gut microbiome, with the dominance of "bad" gut bacteria. Bovine colostrum contains immunoglobulins and beneficial antibodies that can specifically plug those holes in the leaky gut and alter the microbiome population[15]. Additionally, dogs who were supplemented with bovine colostrum had higher levels of plasma antibodies to the Canine Distemper Virus vaccine, suggesting its immunomodulatory effects outside of the gut[15].

Conditions indicated for:

- o Inflammatory bowel disease
- o Pancreatitis
- o Skin allergies
- o Chronic drug use; eg. NSAIDs

vii.   Mushrooms

Dogs can eat mushrooms! There are thousands of species of mushrooms. The varieties that we consume are safe and have similar health benefits for our furry companions. Some mushrooms that grow in the wild are toxic, and for that reason we avoid them. Culinary mushrooms like Button, Shiitake, Swiss Brown, Portobello and Enoki are grown commercially and are common staple in most kitchens. Turkey Tail, Lion's Mane, Reishi, Cordyceps and Chaga mushrooms are considered to harbour valuable medicinal properties. In our modern society, they are usually available in either a liquid extract or granulated (powder) form.

Mushrooms are known for their immune boosting and modulating effects[17], owing to the presence of many polysaccharides which often have synergistic effects when eaten together with other mushroom types. All medicinal mushrooms have potent anti-inflammatory and anti-cancer properties. Turkey Tail mushroom for example, has been proven for its use in dogs with splenic tumours (haemangiosarcoma[18]), increasing survival rates as well as an effective adjunct to chemotherapy. Medicinal mushrooms have a vital role to play in most human and canine degenerative conditions[19]. Caution must be exercised when using medicinal mushroom supplements in individuals who are deficient, such as a decreased appetite, frequent loose stools, low body muscle mass and chilly in general. Mushrooms have strong tonifying effects which can be overwhelming for the unprepared gut. Always start with a quarter of the recommended dosage and work your way upwards over several weeks. Their strong effects on invigorating circulation can also result in frequent bowel movements.

Most common therapeutic applications in companion pets are cancers, skin allergies, autoimmune and kidney diseases. In the recent years I have also noticed more pet owners using them prophylactically as a health supplement.

Mushrooms and their main roles:

- **Reishi**
  - Stress, Sleep, Anti-allergic[20], Liver diseases[20]

- **Cordyceps**
  - Anti-inflammatory, Anti-oxidative, Diabetes[21,22]

- **Turkey Tail**
  - Gut healing, Immunochemotherapeutic agent[23]

- **Shiitake**
  - Digestive and Cardiovascular health[24]

- **Lion's Mane**
  - Cognitive function, Neuro-regenerative, Antisenescence[25]

- **Chaga**
  - Anti-viral[26], Longevity (*anti-DNA mutation[27]*)

Conditions indicated for:

- Kidney insufficiency/ disease
- Cancers
- Autoimmune diseases
- Environmental skin allergies
- Cognitive dysfunction

viii.   Fermented foods

Fermentation refers to the natural and biological method of food preservation, mostly derived from vegetables, dairy and fruits. Foods produced this way are safe to consume due to antimicrobial end-products like ethanol, organic acids and bacterins[28]. Some common examples are yoghurt, cheese, sauerkraut, kimchi, kefir, kombucha, pickles, tempeh and miso. Fermented food offers a source of beneficial microorganisms and prebiotics, which are necessary for improving gastrointestinal tract resilience, metabolism and overall immunity.

Dogs can reap very similar health benefits as much as humans do from including fermented foods in their diet. Supplementing kefir can positively impact gut health by modulating the intestinal microbiome and reducing growth of potential "bad" microbes[29]. Kefir, like most other fermented foods, are affordable and easily accessible. Overgrowth of "bad" microbes such as *Fusobacteriacae*, *Clostridiaceae* and *Ruminococcaceae* are commonly detected in individuals with inflammatory bowel disease and dysbiosis[30]. Dysbiosis refers to the significant alteration of gut microbiome, causing vomiting and/or diarrhea. Common type of drugs that can induce dysbiosis include non-steroidal anti-inflammatories[31] (Meloxicam, Carprofen) and proton pump inhibitors[32] (Omeprazole). Fermented foods have proven immense value and potential when used as a natural additive for preventive health.

In Chinese Medicine, fermented foods have a sour flavour which guides to the Liver, benefitting disorders related to the Liver and Gallbladder systems – such as anxiety, ear infections, gastric reflux and inflammatory bowel syndromes.

Although fermented foods contain a good source of beneficial probiotics, dogs with severe gastrointestinal disease or on long term antibiotics should not rely solely nor expect fermented foods to be of immediate therapeutic significance. Instead, in my experience, a good quality probiotic with a concentration greater than 5 billion

CFU per bacteria specie should be used. In the short term, the probiotics will help replenish the depleted microbiome quickly. *CFU stands for Colony Forming Unit, a method to estimate the number of viable bacteria.*

Conditions indicated for:

- o Inflammatory bowel disease
- o Pancreatitis
- o Skin allergies
- o Ear infections
- o Pododermatitis (paw inflammation/infection)
- o Chronic drug use; eg. NSAIDs

ix. Kidney Beans

In general, beans are not typically mentioned in modern canine nutrition. They are a valuable source of non-digestible fermentable compounds that have anti-inflammatory effects. They have also shown to enhance the gut barrier integrity and mitigate severity of inflammation in the colon (colitis), by downregulating inflammatory receptors[33]. Colitis is extremely common especially in puppies and the general population of dogs. Symptoms are often acute diarrhea without changes in appetite nor energy levels.

When incorporated as part of food therapy in Chinese medicine, they possess a broader meaning and purpose in treating several chronic digestion-related disorders. Kidney beans should be cooked and preferably mashed up to optimise digestibility. The main reason for including kidney beans is due to their *damp* draining properties. Individuals who harbour excess damp tend to have loose stools with mucous coatings, increased flatulence or a stomach that makes rumbly noise frequently. Resembling the shape of kidneys, kidney beans also tonify the *Kidney* system and replenish *Jing* (essence) – meaning they are also indicated for dogs who may have *Kidney* deficiencies (urinary incontinence, lower back weakness, osteoarthritis).

Conditions indicated for:

- Kidney insufficiency/disease
- Urinary incontinence
- Osteoarthritis
- Lower back weakness
- Colitis (*diarrhea without loss of appetite*)

x. Turmeric

Turmeric is a type of culinary spice widely used in Southeast Asia, India and China. More importantly, it has also been used to treat common inflammatory conditions including tumours, biliary diseases, sinusitis, and liver diseases[34]. Curcumin, the bioactive compound extracted from turmeric, has extensive anti-inflammatory, anti-viral, anti-bacterial, immunomodulatory, antioxidative, anticarcinogenic and anti-fibrotic properties. It also has protective effects on the kidneys, liver, cardiovascular and nervous system[34]. Curcumin's bioavailability when taken orally is generally poor due to its low solubility in water. Our body (and the canine gut) simply cannot absorb curcumin well enough. In humans, the bioavailability is improved using pharmaceutical methods such as lipid-based carriers, solid dispersion techniques, etc[34,35]. In dogs, its absorption can be enhanced by simply dissolving turmeric powder in an oil-based medium, such as coconut oil. This is commonly known as the *Golden paste*.

The *Golden paste* is well tolerated by dogs when mixed through their meals. In recent years, it has become a popular adjunct remedy for osteoarthritis, cancers, liver diseases, and most inflammatory skin conditions – largely due to its wide safety margin and low cost. Using turmeric does not replace pharmaceutical medications however it can help reduce reliance on drugs. It also exhibits synergistic benefits when given concurrently with chemotherapeutic drugs, such as in the case of mammary tumours[36]. Turmeric can also slow down the progression of debilitating diseases like Degenerative Myelopathy[37], a fatal disease currently without therapeutic options.

A few important rules when making the *Golden paste*:
- Use only stainless-steel pots and utensils.
- It should only take you 5 minutes to make.
- Store in an airtight container, best in the refrigerator.
- Lasts around 4 weeks in the refrigerator.
- Can be frozen on its own, or mixed with yoghurt.
- Ratio of turmeric powder to water is always 1:2.

Here's my recipe:

1 cup water
½ cup organic turmeric powder
¼ cup coconut oil
1 teaspoon of ground/cracked black pepper

I. *Mix turmeric powder and water in a pot over <u>low heat</u> until it forms a paste.*
II. *Add black pepper and coconut oil.*
III. *Turn off heat and transfer into a glass jar for storage.*

Dosage of the Golden paste depends on the purpose it is used for - pain management, cancer or general wellbeing. It also depends on any concurrent pain medications and resilience of the digestive system.

A general rule of thumb is to start at ½ a teaspoon per 10-15kg dog weight, per day.

If well accepted and tolerated, dogs can have them twice daily at the same dose rate.

Conditions indicated for:

- o Cancers
- o Spinal injuries
- o Osteoarthritis
- o Autoimmune diseases
- o Liver disease

10. ANTI-PARASITIC

Parasitic prevention using natural foods is often the most cost-effective method and something pet parents have absolute control over. Feeding an appropriate diet will strengthen the immune system, increasing host defense against any potential intestinal parasites as well as making them less favourable to fleas or ticks. Keep the immediate environment clean and be aware of what your dog may try to eat on a walk. In a suburban environment, dogs can only get intestinal worms via ingesting worm eggs within dog faeces. Another (unlikely) scenario would be feasting on a dead cow or sheep carcass' diseased organs. Accidental ingestion of a small number of oocysts does not always translate to a full-blown parasitic infestation as it also requires a fairly subdued immune system. Individuals who may be more susceptible include those with chronic inflammatory bowel, cancers or drug-induced immunosuppression. This explains the importance of a fresh diet for preventive health.

Top 3 natural ways:
- Pumpkin seeds
- Garlic
- Dehydrated ears or skin with fur on (kangaroo, cow, rabbit)

i. Pumpkin seeds

Many pet parents would likely have fed their dogs cooked pumpkin, for reasons such as digestive upsets. However, only a very small percentage of people I know actually keep the seeds aside for other reasons. Raw or baked pumpkin seeds, provides a decent amount of insoluble dietary fibre per serve. As the fibre cannot be broken down and used by the body, it is a source of food for gut bacteria as well as a physical deterrent for intestinal worms. In one study[38], the anthelmintic efficacy of pumpkin seeds was 85% compared to ivermectin's 91% (chemical treatment).

Baking the seeds removes moisture which increases the shelf life. They can also be fed raw. For dogs smaller than 15 kg, it is best to put the seeds through a food processor briefly such that they are at least broken into halves.

How often do we incorporate pumpkin seeds? 4-5 seeds per 10 kg dog weight, every two to four weeks as required. More is fine as long as bowel movements are regular.

ii. **Garlic**

Garlic is extensively researched for its antiparasitic[39], antibacterial and antifungal properties. Garlic is safe to feed, as long as we keep it under 5% of a dog's daily diet. In fact, garlic is often listed as one of the ingredients on most commercially sold dog rolls, likely as a natural preservative. Garlic, as noted earlier under "damp-draining properties of foods", is extremely heating. Its pungent nature means it invigorates and moves circulation. Considering all its properties, eating too much garlic may result in some self-limiting diarrhea. Individuals or dogs with excess heat signs should ideally avoid garlic; such as those with excess panting, thirst, tiring easily in the heat and sensitive skin with recurring hot spots.

How does 5% translate to actual weight? Say we feed 3% bodyweight of a 10 kg dog, which equates to 300g of food per day. 5% of 300g = 15g. A garlic clove weighs between 2-4g, which constitutes only about 1% of the dog's daily diet.

My recommendation for prevention of intestinal worms is to incorporate approximately 2g of raw garlic, per 10 kg dog weight, weekly to fortnightly. Note that if your dog has a mostly indoor and sedentary lifestyle, the risk of contracting intestinal worms is extremely low. Garlic is great however may not always be indicated. For dogs who have a higher exposure, such as those who live together with livestock, consider a balanced fresh diet together with other physical deterrents such as pumpkin seeds and dehydrated hides (discussed in next section). Garlic can be used intermittently. For severe infestation of intestinal worms resulting in persistent diarrhea and weight loss, I recommend using a chemical oral dewormer. A faecal egg count by your veterinarian is necessary before reassessing the need for any potential repeat treatments.

iii.   Dehydrated ears or skin with fur

Ears or skin from kangaroo, cows, goats and rabbits serve as a great chewing snack with both mental and physical benefits. They can be fed daily. The dehydration process makes them crispy and chewy at the same time. Containing only skin and cartilage, the caloric content is minimal. Fur or hair is indigestible, like feathers from a bird, hence they are either regurgitated or excreted in faeces. Fur intertwined amongst digesta and faecal material is akin to a bottle brush, cleaning out any oocysts and worms that may have attempted to hold onto the inner mucosal surface of the intestinal walls. This is nature's way of reducing parasitic load in wild predators.

11. DETOXIFYING

Eating foods that can naturally help our bodies detoxify has become increasingly relevant, especially with the continual push from veterinarians to feed dogs highly processed dry diets, routine anti-parasitic chemical prophylaxis, early neutering and recommendation of regular vaccination programs instead of titre-testing. *Titre-test is a blood test to assess antibodies level.* A Liver system that gets little help from processed and refined diets means they are more likely to be overwhelmed and succumb to lapses in immunity. This itself creates a whole new myriad of imbalances, resulting in more ailments presenting in younger dogs.

We know that certain food processing methods generate more free radicals and carcinogens. In the modern human world, the rise in availability and consumption of processed foods has led to a steep increase in autoimmune diseases, food intolerances, anxiety, attention disorders, cancers, poorer health and an increase reliance on pharmaceutical drugs for chronic diseases. The advancement of technology and science seemed to have shifted our lifestyles away from the very basic practice of eating wholesome foods. Whole foods contain natural forms of vitamins, various essential fatty acids, phytonutrients and pigment compounds which are used by the body to combat inflammation and achieve homeostasis. Below is a list of foods you can incorporate into your dog's diet for the purpose of detoxification.

o   Spirulina
o   Chlorella

- o Wheatgrass
- o Celery
- o Mung beans (*must be soaked and boiled*)
- o Kale
- o Apple cider vinegar
- o Broccoli

Comment: Kale should be avoided in dogs with calcium oxalate kidney or bladder stones.

12. THE 5 FLAVOURS AND ELEMENTAL DISORDERS

In the Five Elements Theory discussed earlier, each element is associated with a flavour - sweet, salty, sour, pungent and bitter. Flavours are recognized for their unique properties in guiding food or herbs into a specific organ or channel, for healing purposes.

The 5 elemental flavours:
-   Water (Kidney/Bladder) = salty
-   Fire (Heart/Small Intestine) = bitter
-   Earth (Spleen/Stomach) = sweet
-   Wood (Liver/Gallbladder) = sour
-   Metal (Lung/Large Intestine) = pungent

Salty foods have downward actions, guiding towards the kidneys and bladder. They also help soften masses or nodules. Examples are miso, seaweed, kelp and pickles. The bitter flavour guides to the Heart and is associated with drying and clearing actions. It helps to clear heat from the body, reducing inflammation. Examples of bitter foods are dark leafy greens such as kale, dandelion greens, collard greens (a type of cabbage) and chamomile. Sweet foods are nourishing and tonifying in general, especially beneficial for the digestive system; the Spleen/Stomach systems. In Chinese Medicine, the term sweet does not refer to the sweetness of refined sugar, instead to foods such as rice, dates, red beans, carrots and pumpkin.

Sour foods are associated with the Liver and Gallbladder systems, and have an inward directing effect. The effect is astringent.

Examples are vinegar, sauerkraut, fermented foods and pickles. Pungent foods on the other hand, are outward directing and is associated with the Lung element. They increase circulation and help release the exterior. The best way to describe this is to imagine eating spicy foods and breaking out in sweat! Examples are ginger, garlic, fennel, cinnamon.

Food therapy is complex yet can also be simple. Remember that there are no one-size fits-all diet. Even the most nourishing foods must be eaten in moderation, otherwise we create an imbalance unintentionally. Consider the root imbalance of each individual and choose particular foods in the respective categories. Understanding specific elemental disorder will allow us to enhance results by incorporating flavours.

In this chapter I have categorized various common conventional disease names under each of the five elements. Chinese Medicine addresses the root elemental disorder, regardless of the western medical diagnosis. As the classical saying goes, "different disease, one treatment, multiple treatments, one disease".

Kidney element disorders
1. Kidney disease
2. Diabetes mellitus / insipidus
3. Thyroid (*under functioning and over-active*)
4. Adrenal (*hypo; Addison's disease, or hyper; Cushing's syndrome*)
5. Prostate (*benign hyperplasia; enlargement*)
6. Osteoarthritis (*Bi syndromes*)
7. Deafness
8. Hindquarter weakness
9. All congenital diseases

Kidney & Lung disorders

10. Laryngeal paralysis;

> also known as *Geriatric Onset Laryngeal Paralysis and Polyneuropathy (GOLPP), due to concurrent hindquarter weakness.*

All endocrine diseases (diabetes, thyroid disorders, Addison's and Cushing's) fall under the *Kidney* umbrella. Addison's and Cushing's both relate to the adrenal system, which sits adjacent to the kidneys. The thyroid gland is often referred to as the third kidney in Chinese Medicine, as it plays a central role in metabolism, digestion and balance of other endocrine systems. Osteoarthritis and hindquarter weakness relate to degenerative processes associated with natural ageing. Our Kidney system stores *Jing* (essence), and ailments associated with natural ageing is merely a reflection of unavoidable *Jing* depletion. Individuals born with deficient *Jing* may present with congenital issues such as hip and elbow dysplasia, cleft palates, cryptorchidism and any other growth-related deformities. The Kidney's sensory organ is the ear, so deafness is a sign of a less robust *Qi* or *Jing*. A classic example of this would be Staffordshire Bull Terriers who have an entirely white haircoat, non-pigmented eyelids and are born deaf.

Laryngeal paralysis (LP) typically occurs in older dogs. Certain breeds like Retrievers are predisposed. Robust Kidney Qi is required to anchor the descending Lung Qi, allowing for normal respiratory function. Deficiency in Lung Qi leads to a partial or complete collapse of the laryngeal folds, causing respiratory difficulties and coughing. LP is generally made worse or more pronounced in hot weathers due to the need to pant. A declining Kidney Qi (with age) may also cause concurrent hindquarter weakness. LP typically happens around the same time as progressive weakness in the lower back. This is also why the group of symptoms is now known as GOLPP.

Bladder disorders

1. Urinary tract infections
2. Cystitis (*inflammation without infection*)
3. Urinary crystals/ stones
4. Transitional Cell Carcinoma (*cancer*)

Bladder is the paired organ system with Kidney, within the Water element. Disorders within the bladder are often related to an excess imbalance, such as Dampness & Heat. Recurring urinary tract infections, bladder stones and bladder cancer will also have underlying deficiencies which needs to be supported. Foods that drain Damp and clears Heat should be used in the acute phase of the problem, such as mushrooms, celery and radish. Mushrooms, harbouring multiple properties, can also tonify Qi & improve immunity, meaning they are extra beneficial in cases of recurring infections or immunosuppression.

Urinary crystals and bladder stones reflect the later stages of accumulated heat and extreme dryness (*deficient Yin*). This is often due to eating too much highly processed dry foods, with the complete lack of any other wholesome foods to offset the heat. Due to the hot and dry nature of dry diets, the body overdraws on the *Yin* reserves to maintain homeostasis, eventually generating a huge imbalance. Crystals and stones eventually precipitate.

Liver & Spleen (digestion) disorders

1. Inflammatory bowel disease (IBD)
2. Pancreatitis
3. Colitis
4. Gastric reflux
5. Exocrine pancreatic insufficiency (EPI)
6. Skin allergies

7. Anxiety

<u>Liver & Gallbladder disorders</u>
8. Ear infections (*otitis externa*)
9. Conjunctivitis (*eyes inflammation*)
10. Skin allergies (*paw, groin & ear inflammation*)
11. Erratic or unpredictable behaviour (*irrational decision making*)
12. Liver failure +/- jaundice
13. Gallbladder stones

<u>Liver & Kidney disorders</u>
14. Endometritis
15. Pyometra

The Liver element is involved across multiple disease processes, such as fifteen of the above. Liver's main functions are:
- governs the circulation of *Qi* in the twelve meridians,
- regulates the digestion (*Earth element - Spleen/Stomach*),
- detoxification (emotions and physical)

Most digestive disorders are never primarily gut related only. If there is concurrent anxiety or noise sensitivity, the Liver must be considered in the treatment plan. Anxiety is a reflection of Liver stagnancy. In other words, an anxious individual holds on to unnecessary emotional tension. Prolonged stagnation leads to over-controlling of the Earth element, which weakens it and cause digestive upsets. Liver - Spleen disharmony is an extremely common root imbalance in veterinary patients, regardless of its presentation as gastric reflux, IBD, colitis, pancreatitis and/or skin allergies. Conventional western therapies should be utilized in the short term to address acute symptoms, providing rapid comfort and pain relief where necessary. For skin allergies, inflammation in the groin, paws, ears and conjunctivitis all reflect excess heat within the Liver channel.

Ear infections, especially recurring ones, refer to an excess Dampness and Heat in the Gallbladder channel. In acupuncture, the Gallbladder meridian circles around the ears. However, dogs may not always just have ear infections as the sole problem. Remember that Gallbladder is the paired organ with Liver within the Wood element. If there are any history of sensitive digestion, gastric reflux, chewing paws or skin rashes, then the main focus should be largely on the Liver and the gut. This means eating green and sour foods, such as leafy vegetables, apple cider vinegar, fermented cabbages, kelp, spirulina and chlorella. Leafy greens, cucumbers, watermelons and pears are mostly helpful to clear excess heat, due to their cooling nature. The sour flavour guides & benefits both the Liver & Gallbladder systems.

Endometritis and pyometra (septic inflammation of the uterus) are both potentially fatal and acute diseases which must be addressed with modern medicine. For breeding bitches who developed these conditions, whether or not they have had prior pregnancies, requires attention from an integrative veterinarian to balance out both the Liver and Kidney systems for preventive health.

Heart disorders
1. Mitral/Tricuspid Valvular Disease (heart murmurs)
2. Congestive heart failure
3. Hypertension
3. Anxiety

Disorders within the Heart element tends to be more obvious and straightforward, as they mainly relate to the physical heart organ. Patients with heart diseases will often benefit from supplementing

70

Coenzymes Q10 and increasing intake of essential fatty acids from sources such as oily fish or fish/salmon/krill oil capsules. Other necessary nutrients such as taurine, carnitine, alpha-linolenic acid are abundant in fresh diets, particularly raw hearts and livers. Foods that have a bitter flavour, such as kale, celery, collard greens and burdock root, guide to the Heart.

Lung disorders
1. Collapsing trachea
2. Upper respiratory tract infection / cough
3. Bronchitis
4. Dynamic airway disease
5. Sinusitis
6. Seasonal allergies

Disorders within the Lung element are not as straightforward with food therapy. Eating an appropriate diet will help reduce severity of symptoms though most issues will require intervention from either a pharmacological or herbal medicine point of view. Collapsing trachea, bronchitis, dynamic airway disease all can reflect a deficiency in Lung Qi. Crocodile meat is great at nourishing Lung Qi. Chronic sinusitis with clear thick nasal discharge reflects excess phlegm with concurrent Qi deficiency. Foods that help transform phlegm (almonds, pears) and invigorate Qi will be useful to improve circulation and expel discharge.

Autoimmune diseases

1. Skin – Pemphigus foliaceus (PF), Discoid Lupus Erythematosus (DLE), Systemic Lupus Erythematosus (SLE)
2. Immune mediated haemolytic anaemia (IMHA)
3. Pannus (*chronic superficial keratitis; CSK*)
4. Dry eye (*keratoconjunctivitis sicca; KCS*)

Autoimmune diseases reflect a multi-elemental disorder. Integrative veterinary treatment is often targeted at the predominant imbalance at time of examination. The fundamental rule with all autoimmune diseases is to avoid or lessen intake of processed foods. IMHA patients are anaemic due to destruction of red blood cells. Therefore, foods that nourishes Blood, such as beef, livers, dates, hearts, sardines and eggs are recommended. Both Pannus and dry eye syndrome are often chronic disease processes. In Chinese Medicine they relate to a deficiency in (*Liver and Kidney*) *Yin*; inability to produce sufficient bodily fluids to moisten. In these instances, foods that support both *Liver and Kidney Yin* can further enhance the results of any ongoing treatments. PF, DLE and SLE are reflections of pathogenic *Heat* trapped in the deepest level of the body; long term herbal therapy with or without immunosuppressants are most effective at managing clinical symptoms. Regardless of the disease, food therapy should always be flexible with a variety of foods that can treat the primary imbalance as well as support the individual's other needs.

13.   RAW FEEDING FOR ADULT DOGS – D.I.Y

Having control and flexibility over our dogs' meals not only enhances the human-animal bond, it also eliminates any doubts we have about the quality of pet food purchased off the shelves. Knowing what we can and cannot feed forms the very fundamentals of companion animal nutrition, and is immensely empowering for all pet parents. I commonly see dogs having home-cooked meals when they have been ill; an instinctive human action and general veterinary advice. However, when dogs recover, they revert onto a highly processed dry diet, only to potentially undo all the hard work. To put ourselves in the best position to grow a robust immunity and reduce illnesses, we can all make appropriate dietary choices from the moment your pup step foot into your home.

In the first chapter of this book, I discussed about the canine ancestral diet which contains approximately 54% protein and 45% fat. To derive this level of protein and fat from a fully raw diet, it is only possible to derive from animal sources, not plants. Legumes, nuts and grains also contains an abundance of protein and fat. However, raw grains and nuts are not easily digested without undergoing some form of processing.

An alternative and easier way to put parts of the diet together is to think about a prey model. A small mammal such as a rodent, averages about 70-80% meat, 8% organs, 5-8% bones and a small percentage of digesta containing plant material, grains, nuts and fruits. A healthy adult dog requires at least roughly 10% of raw bones in their diet to satisfy the minimum calcium requirement. Depending on type of bones and bones from different animals, calcium density, eventual digestibility and absorption will vary. For example, poultry bones are light and are mostly hollow in structure, meaning they tend to be broken down and digested a lot faster than a denser bone such as kangaroo tails or spinal bones from cows. The dietary ratio between calcium and phosphorus, as well as Vitamin D, play significant roles in determining how much calcium can be absorbed.

It does not make sense to calculate and feed exact amounts of raw bones to get the calcium and phosphorus ratios perfectly right every single day. Depending on the type of raw meaty bones, they contain meat that is not straightforward to account for. The body is dynamic and have varying nutritional requirements from day to day, depending on stage of growth and level of activity. The calcium to phosphorous ratios in 100g of chicken carcass may be equivalent to only 60g of kangaroo tail, or 80g of lamb ribs.

Follow these **five important steps** and the rest will fall into place.

- Weigh your dog and feed between 2 – 3% bodyweight, per day
- Raw bones (without meaty component) = 10%
- Offal = 10%
- Vegetables and fruits = 10%
- The rest is meat

Take 3% of your dog's weight.

That will be the total volume of food per day.

3% of a 10kg dog is 300g, including the weight of any raw meaty bones.

The rule of thumb is to have approximately 10% of raw bones (minus the meat attached to bones) as part of the dog's total daily intake, and monitor consistency of bowel motions. This will account for feeding different types of bones. Some dogs may have difficulty digesting denser and more challenging bones, resulting in harder and drier stools. What this means is that we simply adjust the frequency of feeding raw meaty bones. Increase the interval between bones to every other day, twice weekly or even once weekly especially if feeding a larger meaty bone. Every dog is different so it is important to learn and understand your dog's eating habits. Remember, balance in diet is achieved over a period of time, weeks and months, never by per day basis.

Commonly fed raw meaty bones and their approximate bone percentage:
- Chicken necks = 35%
- Chicken wing = 45%
- Chicken carcass excluding head and feet = 25%
- Beef ribs = 50%
- Lamb ribs = 30%
- Pig's tail = 30%

To put numbers into perspective, a 10kg dog eats about 300g of food daily (using 3% bodyweight as an example). Assuming she gets two equal meals a day, if we feed 150g of chicken necks for breakfast, the bone component in that diet will be 17.5% (35% divided by 2). However, if we include just 75g (half of 150g) of chicken necks, then her diet will consist around 9% of raw bones, which is much closer to the ideal 10%.

Similarly, if we fed 150g of beef ribs, then there will be 25% bone in her overall intake. Feeding 75g will reduce bone to 12.5%, which will be theoretically sound as it is still very close to 10%. However, as mentioned earlier, beef ribs as compared to chicken necks, have a higher bone density and may require a more robust digestive system to prevent constipation. Instead of feeding 75g, it will be safer and wise to perhaps feed lesser (eg. 50g) and monitor bowel movements.

If raw bones cannot be fed for any reasons, a natural calcium source such as eggshell powder should be used. As it is nature's calcium, the actual concentration of calcium per teaspoon of grounded eggshell will vary. Following the same principles as with feeding raw meaty bones, it is impossible to feed an exact amount of calcium unless it is from a synthetic source. The recommendation for eggshell powder is roughly one level metric teaspoon, per 30kg dog weight, per day.

The general rule for calcium intake is approximately 100mg/kg of body weight /day. One level teaspoon of eggshell powder typically contains between 2500 – 3000mg of calcium.

Other calcium (Ca) supplementation options:

Calcium carbonate: 1 teaspoon = 1200mg Ca
Calcium citrate: 1 teaspoon = 420mg Ca
Dicalcium phosphate: 1 teaspoon = 1200 – 1600mg Ca

Offal

Now that you have figured out how much meaty bones (roughly!) you can or should include in the diet, here comes the easy part. Offal must form between 5-10% of the diet, for essential vitamins and trace minerals such as iron, copper, manganese, selenium, B vitamins, etc. For healthy individuals the aim is 10%. Some dogs who may be more sensitive may only need and tolerate 5%, or less. Using the same example of a 10kg dog getting fed 300g of food daily, 10% of offal will be 30g.

Livers from cows, sheep and pigs are my preferred options. Where feasible, rotate between livers, hearts, pancreas and kidneys. Dogs suffering from severe inflammatory bowel disease should ideally avoid offal initially, especially if bowel movements are unpredictable. In my experience, dehydrated livers seemed to be less volatile and can be safely introduced in small amounts. Due to the dehydration process, only moisture is removed whilst retaining most of its nutrients. If including offal as part of a cooked diet, attempt to cook it as gently as possible. For instance, thinly slice up pieces of liver and add to the pot of cooked meat and/or vegetables last, either on a low heat for only a few minutes, then allowing the residual heat to cook through.

Vegetables and fruits

Vegetables and fruits are not typically part of a canine's diet so dogs can do well without inclusion of much greens at all. However, considering the less robust average genetic pool amongst various breeds and our increased usage with chemicals and drugs, phytonutrients can be extremely helpful to reduce risk of diseases and cancers. They also contain an abundance of dietary fibre (prebiotics), which provides food for the gut microbiome and ensures consistent bowel movements. Afterall, we all wish for our dogs to live for as long and as healthy as possible.

Vegetables need to be partially digested or processed in a blender to allow maximal absorption. Dogs lack cellulase, the enzymes that all herbivores possess, to break down the cellular wall of plant material. Dogs also don't chew vegetables like herbivores or humans do, so it is important for us to allow any vegetables to be readily digestible and absorbed. The act of chewing, blending or finely chopping merely increases the surface area for optimal digestibility.

Examples of vegetables and grains that I commonly include in a dog's diet:

- Spinach
- Peas
- Carrots
- Broccoli
- Pumpkin
- Sweet potato
- Cauliflower
- Kidney beans
- Black beans
- Kale
- Celery
- Radish
- Bok Choy
- Silver beet

As part of the family, most dogs enjoy a piece or two of fruit. Fruits also possess energetic properties such as heating or cooling, which can be used accordingly to your dog's advantage to further support any of his/her imbalances. Note that grapes and its derivatives (raisins, sultanas, grape seed extracts) must be avoided due to the presence of tannic acid, which is toxic to their kidneys. All other fruits can be shared safely with your canine companion.

Cooling fruits:

- Strawberry
- Kiwi fruit
- Blueberry
- Apples
- Banana
- Mango

- Pear
- Watermelon
- Orange

Warming fruits:
- Blackberry
- Papaya
- Peach
- Cherry
- Apricot

Neutral:
- Pineapple
- Figs
- Lemon

Phlegm transforming:
- Apple
- Pear
- Grapefruit peel
- Lemon

Comment: Always take care when feeding stone fruits. Seeds must be discarded away from your dog's reach. Seeds from stone fruits such as mangoes and apricots are common causes of intestinal obstruction.

Using the earlier example using raw chicken necks as the bone component, a 10kg dog will have around 75g chicken necks per day. 10% of offal and vegetables respectively adds up to 60g. The remaining volume will contain a combination of meat, fish and eggs. For example, 300g – 75g – 60g = 165g of meat.

Using this formula, you would simply multiply each component accordingly to make a larger quantity. Mix well together and portion into individual meals, prior freezing. This should form the main bulk of your dog's diet. However, to balance out the diet over time, there needs to be at least two to three variations between animal proteins. Ensure you also incorporate the following for completeness.

> ➤ Chicken eggs; raw
> ➤ Fish – sardines, tuna, mackerel (*raw or in spring water*)
> ➤ Flaxseed/ Linseed meal (*prebiotics*)

Chicken eggs

As mentioned under the Superfoods chapter, eggs contain certain nutrients (choline, Vitamin D, selenium, Vitamin B12) that a predominantly meat-based diet lacks. As these nutrients are required in smaller quantities, adding an egg once or twice weekly is generally adequate. Dogs can also eat eggs daily should pet owners wish to give more. Note that dogs do not suffer cholesterol related issues like humans do. Eggshells can be crushed and added to the meal. Remember that the shells are excellent natural sources of calcium!

Fish

Oily fish like sardines, salmon, tuna and mackerel are excellent sources of protein. Importantly, they contain natural derivatives of essential omega fatty acids that are highly bioavailable and crucial for many health functions. These include cardiovascular health, kidney function, neuromuscular and cognitive function. EPA (eicosapentaenoic acid) and DHA (docosahexaenoic acid) are both long chain polyunsaturated fatty acids that are considered essential, meaning dogs must obtain them from diet. For example, alpha-linolenic acid (ALA) is a plant-based short chain fatty acid found in flaxseeds (and its oils), hemp seeds and pumpkin seeds. In a human body, ALA can be converted to EPA and DHA via delongase and desaturase enzymes, albeit in very small amounts. However, dogs do not possess the enzymes needed for the conversion. Dogs also have a much quicker gut transit time than humans, meaning food is broken down and passed through the gastrointestinal tract faster. Conversion between types of dietary fats requires time, appropriate enzymes and mechanisms, all of which the canine gut lacks.

An alternative is using fish/krill/salmon oil capsules. Note that fish oil sold in the market are often labelled as 1000mg or 2000mg. We need to actually look at the EPA and DHA concentration (in mg). Fish oil in the lower range, usually costing lesser, typically have a lower EPA/DHA concentration. An average dog requires a minimum of 40 mg/kg EPA and 30 mg/kg DHA for general health and maintenance. Dogs with osteoarthritis, heart and/or kidney disease may require between 3-5 times higher in dosages to achieve therapeutic anti-inflammatory effects. The flexibility and variation to meet individual's needs, is not possible to achieve with a dry diet.

Dogs with a sensitive digestion, or those who eat a predominantly dry diet, need to pay more attention when introducing oily fish. Natural oils get oxidized and turn rancid when exposed to oxygen, therefore the actual amount of bioavailable essential fatty acids in dry diets is unlikely to reflect what is written on the label. Dogs who are solely fed kibble will never have been exposed to much fatty acids at all. More than often, if your dog cannot fully digest more than two different meat proteins or suffers from frequent loose stools, oily fish should ideally be avoided to prevent aggravation of the gut. They can be slowly introduced later once the gut imbalances have been addressed. A potentially safer alternative is algae oil, which can reduce gut associated adverse effects.

Flaxseed / Linseed meal

Plant based food like vegetables, fruits, nuts and grains contain insoluble and soluble fibre that are designed to regulate the gut microbiome. These fibres are also known as prebiotics. Flaxseed or linseed meal is optional if there is adequate intake of greens. Prebiotics are necessary to feed the good bacteria to build and maintain gut resilience. Dogs who have a picky appetite may reject any vegetable material, regardless of its form – diced, cooked or juiced. In my experience, these individuals often have an undiagnosed underlying deficiency in their gut. They may also have a habit of eating grass or vomiting bile. Adding a pinch of flaxseed meal is often very well tolerated and will go a long way in improving the microbiome which subsequently opens up the appetite.

Recommended dose for flaxseed/linseed meal, per day:

¼ teaspoon for dogs up to 15kg
½ teaspoon for dogs between 15-30kg
¾ teaspoon for dogs between 30-45kg.

Individuals who have a chronic digestive issue will benefit from doubling the above dosage.

14.   FEEDING PUPPIES

Introducing raw meals to a puppy is usually done after weaning –
as nature intended. In wild canids, mother dogs would typically
regurgitate parts of a prey for their young to feed on. As they grow
older, they begin to mimic adults and feast on the remaining parts
of a carcass. The two considerations with a domesticated puppy
diet are feeding according to the percentage of bodyweight at
various growth stages and number of meals per day. Adults eat
between 2 – 3% of their bodyweight. Puppies will need anywhere
between 5 – 8 % bodyweight, depending on the breed and phase of
growth. They also eat multiple times per day, owing to their rapid
metabolism and development.

I have listed some frequently asked questions relating to puppy
diets, with direct answers.

- When should I start introducing raw foods?

    Raw food should ideally be introduced as early as
    possible, exposing the puppy to varying textures and
    flavours in their diet. Early introduction also helps
    increase the gut microbiome's diversity, which is
    crucial for immunity, physical and mental health.
    Many behavioural challenges can also be avoided
    when they have a healthy population of gut
    microbiome, owing to the direct relationship within
    the gut-brain axis; where healthy bacteria increase
    the production of serotonin and other 'happy'
    hormones. Puppyhood is no doubt the golden period
    when we set ground rules and engage in house

training. It should not be any different to their gut health, where we can maximise their growth potential by feeding a specie appropriate fresh diet.

- My puppy came with a diet plan from the breeder, how should I transition?

    Having done your research, you can begin transitioning as soon as you are ready. Diet plans from breeders can vary significantly, and may not be suitable for every dog in different families. Upon weaning, some puppies are fed dry kibble whereas others have been introduced to raw meat. A gradual transition over 3-4 weeks is recommended. This gives us enough time to learn about the pup's feeding and toileting habits. Occasional diarrhea is part and parcel of puppyhood. This can usually be due to stress from relocation, adjusting to new diets as well as geographic factors. As long as their appetite and energy levels remain normal, most gut related problems tend to be self-limiting.

- What type of raw meaty bones can I safely feed?

    The type of raw meaty bones will depend on two things in a puppy. Presence of deciduous (baby) teeth and jaw size. Age of the puppy should not be used as a gauge as it varies significantly between breeds. For example, a 6 months old Jack Russell Terrier versus a 6 months old Bull Arab dog are two dogs at very different stages of growth. If deciduous teeth are still around, softer bones such as chicken wing tips or necks are preferred. As the puppy gets used to chewing you can use lamb or pork ribs for a more challenging bite, also to engage those canines and incisors.

- Can I use a commercially prepared raw diet?

  Yes – as long as it is from a reputable supplier. Most decent pet food manufacturers often have a large customer base in your area. Always do your research and check in with like-minded pet owners.

- Should I only use organic foods and meat products?

  In an ideal world, we would all eat organically grown foods. However, this is not always feasible. Do what you can in terms of affordability and sustainability. Honestly – I wouldn't worry too much about it. Having your puppy on a fresh diet is already a big step in the right direction.

- My puppy won't touch raw food, what can I do?

  Some dogs are just less motivated by food, and there is nothing wrong with that. Try feeding one main meal per day instead of multiple meals. Unfortunately, you cannot force a puppy to eat if they are not interested or hungry enough. If the puppy is on a dry diet, reduce the amount fed per day. Dry kibble should also never be left out all day long for them to graze on. Dry diets often contain carbohydrates in excess of 40% which equals to calories that is filling your pup's stomach up.

  Finally, patience! Every dog is unique in their own ways. If a fully raw diet does not work out, a gently cooked diet is absolutely fine too. At the end of the day, dietary balance is achieved over a period of time, and adjusted according to your puppy's needs.

- Are air-dried or freeze-dried commercial 'raw' diets the same as raw meals?

  Drying methods, whether freezing or air drying, remove moisture entirely from fresh and perishable foods. Dry diets can weigh just a quarter of the original weight of the food. On paper they are comparable nutritionally to actual raw diets and present as convenient options for pet owners. One of the best-selling points is that they are the healthier alternatives to dry kibble and have long shelf lives. This is true.

  In my opinion, once wholesome foods have gone through a drying process, they can never be the same. I have also found that the air dried or freeze-dried versions of raw meals do not have the same effect on healing when it comes to using them in food therapy. They are simply devoid of life force, or *Qi*. The flavours, textures and tastes of an actual fresh raw meals are lost. Satiety is diminished. Water-soluble vitamins are also lost when you remove moisture entirely. The best way I can explain this is to imagine eating dried banana chips or sweet potato crisps, which is never quite the same as eating the real thing on its own! Or eating strips of beef jerky compared to eating a piece of steak.

- Do I need to add any supplements for gut and joint health?

Generally speaking, if you are already feeding a fresh diet with variation, there is little requirement for supplements. Probiotics are safe to incorporate, though there is no need to use them religiously for long periods (> 2 months), especially if the digestion is consistently normal. Veterinary specific joint supplements that contain marine sourced fatty acids such as green lipped mussels, shark cartilage, krill or fish oils are commonly used in larger breed puppies to reduce risk of joint ailments. They can certainly be used although a balanced base diet still plays a far bigger role.

15.   COOKING FOOD FOR MY DOG

There are two variations when formulating a cooked diet, depending on the requirements of each dog – with or without the use of raw meaty bones. Some dogs can tolerate small amounts of raw meaty bones, which is excellent for dental hygiene and a source of dietary calcium. For those that cannot digest raw bones, eggshells or other natural/synthetic calcium sources can be considered.

Dogs who can digest raw meaty bones, even if they are given once, twice or thrice per week, can follow the same guidelines as above. The rest of the meal would be cooked gently.

One important mathematical calculation to note is the difference in the as fed weight of the meal. Raw ingredients tend to be proportionally heavier due to the presence of water. When planning and preparing ingredients, it's only logical to base them on raw weights. For example, I have planned to prepare meals enough for 7 days. My dog weighs 10 kg. I intend to feed 2.5% bodyweight per day, which equals to 250g of food daily. 7 x 250g = 1750g. If I had gathered my raw ingredients totaling to 1750g, I may only get ¾ of what I had initially, due to moisture loss during the cooking process.

To simplify the math, I find it easiest to add between 0.5 - 1% to the intended percentage of body weight. If my dog requires 2.5% body weight of food, I would gather my raw ingredients based on 3 – 3.5%.

The cooking processes

There are three main parts to the diet – meat, organs and vegetables. The easiest way would be to cook all in a crockpot, like a stew or casserole. Alternatively, some may prefer baking into a meatloaf. Remember, there are no right or wrong methods to do it. Any form of cooking will naturally result in the loss of nutrients, due to the heat induced denaturation of enzymes. However, cooked meals are also much easier to digest and are crucial for individuals who are deficient or battling chronic illnesses.

Organs like liver, pancreas and kidneys tend to cook very quickly, especially if they are already thinly sliced. They must be cooked lightly. Vegetables, sweet potato and pumpkin are best steamed separately and then finely chopped up, or processed very briefly in a blender. This method retains maximum nutrients and is gentle on the stomach.

Cooking oil is generally not necessary. Coconut or walnut oil are both excellent choices when required.

Beef & sweet potato recipe without raw meaty bones, for 10kg healthy dog:

200g beef mince
30g beef liver
30g sweet potato
30g leafy greens & choice of fruit
1/3 tsp of eggshell powder
¼ tsp spirulina or kelp powder
¼ tsp flaxseed meal
½ tsp coconut oil

I.   Cut sweet potato into 3cm cubes, with the option of leaving the skin on.

II.   Steam sweet potato with any leafy greens until you can easily inset a chopstick through.

III. Cook beef mince in a pot or pan under low-medium heat. Add coconut oil and mix well until meat turns light brown.

IV.   Add thinly sliced beef livers and mix well for about 3-4 minutes.

V.   Turn off fire.

VI.   Add sweet potato and greens in. Mash and mix thoroughly with a spoon or fork. (Option of putting steamed sweet potato/greens in a food processor for a few seconds before mixing with meat)

VII. Top dress with eggshell powder, spirulina and flaxseed meal prior serving.

The above diet is by no means a fully complete and balanced diet according to the canine nutritional guidelines. The only way we could have balance that out completely to the tee will be to include a synthetic multivitamin tablet and use exact grams instead of approximating using teaspoons. To balance the diet out naturally over time, you will rotate through different proteins, vegetables and fruits. Consider red and white meats, and colorful vegetables like carrots, spinach, cauliflower and broccoli. Using TCVM principles, you can add more value to the diet by choosing foods that are energetically suitable for your dog's imbalances, if any. Grass-fed beef is a neutral protein so is suitable for most dogs unless there is a true intolerance to beef.

16.   RAW MEATY BONES

Including raw meaty bones in your dog's diet will serve three main purposes. Source of dietary calcium, dental hygiene and mental enrichment. Depending on the type of raw bones, they encourage chewing which stimulates production of endorphins, also known as the happy hormone. Bones that vary in shapes and sizes are ideal as they engage different parts of the dental arcade, paying special attention to the canines and incisors, which are designed for apprehending and tearing meat off bones. In my opinion, dry kibble, dental stick chews, water additives and manual brushing of teeth are all ineffective methods in regards to teeth cleaning.

Dogs do not engage their canines or incisors when eating any form of dry kibble. In the case of gobbling down a relatively soft dental chew, the few seconds worth of chewing will certainly not provide any substantial teeth cleaning. Most chews are also elongated in shape, which means they rarely engage the canines or incisors. If your dog allows you to stick a toothbrush into his/her mouth without chewing it off, you may be lucky enough to get away with a few half-hearted scrubs on the outer surface of the teeth. Unfortunately, it is impossible to brush on the inner surfaces of teeth, gum lines, as well as in between each tooth. That makes tooth brushing potentially stressful for both parties involved, as well as being a waste of time. In my decade long career as a veterinarian, I also have not seen results from water additives claiming to help. They might only improve the breath temporarily.

A full dental scale and polish under a general anaesthesia (GA) may be recommended from your local veterinarian, as often as annually. However, speaking from personal experiences, a clean set of teeth usually lasts no longer than 8-10 weeks, especially if there are no ongoing prophylactic methods to maintain the cleanliness. Very few owners would actually be inclined to put their pooches through a full GA every year. Despite acknowledging the safe track records of our current anaesthetic protocols in veterinary patients, ageing and various health conditions such as heart and kidney diseases are common reasons we shy away from a dental clean. Remember, if consenting for a dental clean under a full GA isn't a straightforward yes for a 3-year-old, it will only get harder at 6, and (almost) impossible to say yes when your dog turns 10. It could be too late to introduce any raw bones then if they have never been exposed to them.

Caution 1:
Do not feed weight-bearing bones of cows, sheep and pigs (femur, tibias, humerus) as they tend to splinter. They are also too hard and dense to chew, especially for smaller dogs (<10 kg).

Caution 2:
Do not feed cooked bones as they are indigestible and can potentially cause intestinal blockages.

Choose raw meaty bones that are appropriate for your dog's jaw size.

Small, easy to digest bones:
- Chicken/Duck wing tips, necks, drums, feet, frames
- Lamb ribs

Medium-sized bones:
- Turkey necks, wings
- Pork ribs, vertebrae (spine)
- Pig's tails

Larger, denser bones:
- Beef brisket, ribs
- Beef vertebrae (spine)
- Kangaroo/Ox tail

There are some exceptions to the above guide depending on breed and jaw anatomy. Brachycephalic breeds such as Pugs and Bulldogs may only be able to handle smaller and simpler bones such as poultry wings, regardless of their body weight. This is mainly due to their unique dentition as well as ability to chew efficiently. A good proportion of them may have elongated soft palates that partially obstructs the pharynx, making the act of prolonged chewing and breathing at the same time much more challenging.

Larger breed dogs, such as Retrievers, Mastiffs, Rottweilers and Great Danes will be able to handle most type of raw meaty bones. However, for the purpose of maintaining dental hygiene, bigger and more challenging bones in odd shapes and sizes should be used. These bones include kangaroo tails, beef briskets and ribs. Smaller bones such as poultry necks and feet are more than likely to be swallowed either whole or in halves. It is also not uncommon for dogs to swallow chicken necks or feet whole. The extremely acidic nature of the canine stomach (pH 1 - 1.5) helps them digest raw bones effectively.

Puppies who still have their deciduous (baby) teeth should only get bones that are soft and easy to digest, for safety reasons and also to encourage proper chewing habits. Again, depending on individual breed and jaw size, chicken wing tips and smaller chicken wings are safest to introduce, due to their soft and hollow structures. If your puppy has never eaten a raw meaty bone before, I recommend holding onto it and allowing him/her to chew.

17. FOOD ENERGETICS - QUICK REFERENCE GUIDE

Cooling

- o Rabbit, Duck, Turkey, Shark, Crocodile, Mussels, White Bait, Cod, Frog
- o Spinach, Celery, Broccoli, Cucumber, Alfalfa, White Radish, Seaweed
- o Apple, Kiwi fruit, Mango, Strawberry, Blueberry, Watermelon, Pear, Banana
- o Brown rice, Honey, Mung bean, Tofu, Barley

Neutral

- o Pork, Beef, Quail, Sardines, Tuna, Mackerel, Eel
- o Pork & Beef Livers, Beef Tripe, Pork Kidneys
- o Chicken Egg; whole
- o Cabbage, Cauliflower, Pumpkin, Sweet Potato, Mushrooms, Carrots
- o Kidney beans, Black beans, Green peas, String beans, Black sesame seeds, Dates

Warming/Hot

- o Chicken, Salmon, Prawns, Lobsters (warming)
- o Lamb, Goat, Camel, Kangaroo, Venison, Emu, Horse (hot)
- o Chicken Liver, Beef & Lamb Kidneys, Lamb Livers
- o Blackberry

- Basil, Thyme, Ginger, Garlic, Coriander, Fennel
- Oats, Sorghum, White rice, Olive oil, Apple Cider Vinegar

Qi tonifying

- Rabbit, Pork, Chicken, Beef, Salmon, Mackerel, Eel
- Brown rice, Pumpkin, Sweet Potato, Shiitake Mushrooms, Oats

Blood tonifying

- Beef, Sardines, Chicken eggs, Beef/Pork Livers and Hearts
- Kidney beans, Parsley, Carrots, Dates

Yin tonifying

- Rabbit, Duck, Pork, Chicken eggs, Mussels
- Black beans, Kidney beans, Spinach, Peas, String beans
- Black sesame seeds, Honey, Tofu
- Apples, Pears, Mangoes

Yang tonifying

- Lamb, Venison, Beef/Lamb Kidneys
- Cinnamon bark, Garlic, Dried Ginger, Basil, Rosemary, Fennel, Thyme
- Raspberry

Damp draining

- Apple cider vinegar, Celery, Alfalfa, Kidney Beans, Garlic, Pumpkin, Chamomile

Phlegm transforming

- Almonds, Garlic, Ginger, Seaweed, Thyme, Peppermint, Radish
- Apples, Pears

Stagnation moving

- Chicken, Lamb, Venison
- Parsley, Coriander, Garlic, Ginger, Turmeric, Apple cider vinegar, Dill seeds

18.   TRANSITIONAL DIET FOR INFLAMMATORY BOWEL DISEASE

The following diet is for dogs who may tick most of those boxes below. It is designed to support underlying deficiencies to help dogs transit out of a commercial dry diet. This diet can be fed between 3-6 months. Longer term dietary plans should always be consulted with an integrative veterinarian.

◇   Reliant on corticosteroids (eg. *Prednisolone*) to control diarrhea.
◇   Seem to be able to only eat a commercial low allergenic dry kibble. Any other food will induce diarrhea.
◇   Vomits bile frequently.
◇   Lip licking through the day, tends to worsen overnight.
◇   Poor response to medications such as antacids.
◇   Has needed repeated courses of *Metronidazole* (antibiotic) for episodes of diarrhea in the past.

<u>Example; for 10kg dog, per day.</u>
(Gently cooked)

Meat 150g   (*choose either 1 or 2 proteins only*)
Sweet potato /Pumpkin/ Oats 80g
Carrots/ Broccoli 70g
Spirulina; ¼ tsp
+ Egg, soft boiled (*optional; once per week*)
+ Eggshell powder; ½ tsp

**Foods to avoid during transition:

- Offal,

- Raw bones,

- Oily fish (sardines, salmon and tuna), Fish/Krill oil capsules.

19.   TRANSITIONAL DIET FOR RECURRING EAR INFECTIONS

Recurring ear infections is indicative of excess Dampness and Heat from the Liver system.   This means a raw diet using mostly energetically cooling foods should help. However, this is not always the case. If there is a history of a sensitive digestion, such as occasional retching (gastric reflux) or inconsistent bowel movements, then a cooked diet may be more beneficial.

For dogs with a **robust digestion**, consistent appetite and bowel motions, feed a raw diet using energetically cooling to neutral foods.

- Turkey, Duck, Rabbit, Whiting, Shark, Mussels, Cod, Pork, Beef (grass-fed).

Select foods from the *"Damp draining"* category to increase the value of the diet.
Add a good quality probiotic.

Raw diets can either be commercially prepared, using prey-mixes or D.I.Y as laid out in chapter 13. Remember, raw feeding is designed to be variable and flexible!

For dogs with a **sensitive gut**, their tongues may often appear pale pink or lavender tinged. Excess *Dampness* can also reflect through the hair coat as greasiness with a strong odour. Dogs with more deficiencies may also shed hair easily, or has a tendency to prefer warm places. The focus and priority here should be on strengthening the gut. A cooked diet with an overall neutral energy is recommended.

- Turkey and Salmon combination,
- Beef (grass-fed),
- Duck and Beef combination,
- Mackerel and Beef combination,
- Turkey and Lamb combination.

Add *Damp draining* foods gradually and include a good quality probiotic. Prebiotics such as flaxseed meal is also highly recommended to help strengthen the existing microbiome.

Example: for 10kg dog, per day.

Meat 180g
Offal 10g
Pumpkin 50g
Celery, Alfalfa, Spinach 60g
+ Apple cider vinegar ½ tsp
+ Flaxseed meal ¼ tsp
+ Eggshell powder ½ tsp (*not necessary if raw meaty bones are fed*)

20. TRANSITIONAL DIET FOR KIDNEY DISEASE

Diet should seek to fulfill these requirements:
- ◊   Low phosphorus
- ◊   Adequate essential fatty acids
- ◊   High moisture
- ◊   Adequate calcium
- ◊   High chlorophyll /phytonutrients

Selection of proteins will also highly depend on individual's main deficient pattern, such as *Kidney Qi, Yin or Yang* deficiency.

Qi deficiency
- -   Tongue is generally pale when compared to the gums.
- -   Drinking and urination is not excessive.
- -   Sleeps most parts of the day.
- -   Feels the cold easily.
- -   Weight loss or lean body condition.

- ➢   Chicken, Pork, Beef, Salmon preferred.

Yang deficiency
- -   Yang deficiency happens after prolonged Qi deficiency.
- -   Signs are similar to the above.
- -   Dogs are cold to touch; ears, lower back and extremities.
- -   May also have chronic diarrhea.

➢ Chicken, Lamb, Venison, Mutton, Beef preferred.

Yin deficiency
- Increased thirst and urination.
- Excessive panting, especially at night.
- Have trouble sleeping through the night.
- Seeks cold.
- Dry, flaky coat
- Tongue appears dark red and dry.

➢ Pork, Turkey, Rabbit, Cod, Whiting, Duck are preferred.

Diet can be cooked or raw. A cooked diet is preferred for *Qi* and *Yang* deficiency patterns.

<u>Example; for 10kg dog, per day.</u>

Meat 160g
Offal 20g
Vegetables 60g
Sweet potato/Pumpkin 60g
Eggshell powder; ½ tsp
+ Sardines/Tuna in spring water; 50g twice weekly
+ Spirulina/ Chlorella powder; ¼ tsp

Comment: Dogs with elevated serum Phosphorus should consider adding a phosphorus-binder such as *Calcium Carbonate* or *Aluminium Hydroxide* tablets. Both are non-prescription. Phosphorus is mainly found in meat and high serum Phosphorus puts the kidneys under further stress. This allows dogs to eat a variety of meats without having to worry about the phosphorus content.

21.   TRANSITIONAL DIET FOR CANCERS

In Chinese Medicine, the root of all cancers is a *Qi deficiency* pattern. Without lapses in the immune system, cancers do not happen. Whilst some dogs may still be able to consume a raw diet, a cooked diet is recommended due to its stronger nourishing effect on the gut. Excessive raw foods tend to overconsume *Qi* due to its cold nature. Dogs on chemotherapy should be on a cooked diet due to active immunosuppression.

Carbohydrates can be beneficial by increasing the caloric density of the diet. This helps the dog maintain weight by eating the same volume or lesser. My recommendation is to keep carbohydrates between 10% so we avoid fueling the cancer cells.

Spirulina is one of the superfoods that is a must due to the pigment phycocyanin which has anti-cancer properties. I highly recommend it to be used in conjunction with chemotherapy.

Example; for 10kg dog, per day.

Meat 180g
Offal 30g
Vegetables 60g
Sweet potato, Oats 30g
+ Spirulina; ½ to ¾ tsp
+ Eggshell powder; ½ tsp
+ Egg (soft boiled); 1-2 per week

For cancers that present as large tumours or masses, add:

(eg. *Soft tissue sarcomas, Mast cell tumours, Mammary gland tumours, Gastrointestinal stromal tumours*)

> ➢ Seaweed or Kelp

For Lymphoma, Haemangiosarcoma or Osteosarcoma, add:

> ➢ Medicinal mushrooms (eg. *Turkey Tail*)
> ➢ Turmeric paste

For brain tumours, add:

> ➢ Vitamin E; *500 I.U. per 15-20kg bodyweight*

For respiratory tract or lung tumours, add:

> ➢ Medicinal mushrooms

Comment: Cancer cells like "quick and cheap" energy. Whilst supporting the body with many vitamins and herbs is ideal, it is important not to overload on supplements. I personally try to keep it under three supplements per meal. Anything more should be rotated throughout the week to ensure optimal absorption. This also prevents "supplement fatigue" where the powders or tablets overwhelms the actual meal resulting in a decrease in appetite.

22. REFERENCES

1. Bosch G, Hagen-Plantinga EA, Hendriks WH. *Dietary nutrient profiles of wild wolves: insights for optimal dog nutrition? British Journal of Nutrition. 2015; 113: S40-S54*

2. Association of American Feed Control Officials. *http://www.aafco.org*

3. National Research Council. 2006. *Nutrient Requirements of Dogs and Cats. Washington, DC: The National Academies Press. http://doi.org/10.17226/10668*

4. Hill RC, Choate CJ, Scott KC, et al. *Comparison of the guaranteed analysis with the measured nutrient composition of commercial pet foods. JAVMA. 2009; 234(3): 347-351*

5. Ma Z, Jia C, Guo J, Gu H, Miao Y. *Features analysis of five-element theory and its basal effects on construction of visceral manifestation theory. Journal of Traditional Chinese Medicine 2014; 34(1): 115-121*

6. Fowler M, Xie H. 2020. *Integrative and Traditional Chinese Veterinary Medicine Food Therapy. 1st Edition, Chi University Press, Florida, USA.*

7. Ötleş, S, Pire R. *Fatty Acid Composition of Chlorella and Spirulina Microalgae Species. JF Journal of AOAC INTERNATIONAL 2019; 84(6): 1060-3271. Doi: 10.1093/jaoac/84.6.1708.*

8. Finamore A, Palmery M, Bensehaila S, Peluso I. *Antioxidant, Immunomodulating, and Microbial-Modulating Activities of the Sustainable and Ecofriendly Spirulina. Oxid Med Cell Longev. 2017;*

2017: 3247528. Doi: 10.1155/2017/3247528. Epub
2017 Jan 15. PMID: 28182098; PMCID: PMC5274660.

9. Jiang L, Wang Y, Yin Q, Liu G, Liu H, Huang Y, Li B.
    Phycocyanin: A Potential Drug for Cancer Treatment.
    J Cancer. 2017; 8(17):3416-3429. Doi:
    10.7150/jca.21058. PMID: 29151925; PMCID:
    PMC5687155.

10. Zainul Azlan N, Mohd Yusof YA, Alias E, Makpol
    S. Chlorella vulgaris Improves the Regenerative
    Capacity of Young and Senescent Myoblasts and
    Promotes Muscle Regeneration. Oxid Med Cell Longev.
    2019. 3520789. Doi: 10.1155/2019/3520789

11. Pereira, L., Morrison, L., Shukla, P.S. and Critchley,
    A.T., 2020. A concise review of the brown macroalga
    Ascophyllum nodosum (Linnaeus) Le Jolis. Journal of
    Applied Phycology, 32: 3561-3584.

12. Zhu Q, Chen J, Li Q, Wang T, Li H. Antitumour activity
    of polysaccharide from Laminaria japonica on mice
    bearing H22 liver cancer. International Journal of
    Biological Macromolecules. 2016; 92: 156-158. ISSN
    0141-8130.
    https://doi.org/10.1016/j.ijbiomac.2016.06.090

13. Komosinska-Vassev K, Olczyk P, Kaźmierczak J,
    Mencner L, Olczyk K. 2015. Bee Pollen: Chemical
    Composition and Therapeutic Application, Evidence-
    Based Complementary and Alternative Medicine,
    Article ID 297425.
    https://doi.org/10.1155/2015/297425

14. Shaldoum F, El-kott A F, Ouda M M A, Abd-Ella E M.
    2021. Immunomodulatory effects of bee pollen
    doxorubicin-induced bone marrow/spleen
    immunosuppression in rat. 45(6).
    https://doi.org/10.1111/jfbc.13747

15. Sienkiewicz M, Szymańska P, Fichna J.
    Supplementation of Bovine Colostrum in

Inflammatory Bowel Disease: Benefits and Contraindications, Advances in Nutrition. 2021; 12(2): 533- 545. https://doi.org/10.1093/advances/nmaa120

16. Mabry K, Hill T, Tolbert MK. Prevalence of gastrointestinal lesions in dogs chronically treated with nonsteroidal anti-inflammatory drugs. J Vet Intern Med. 2021 Mar;35(2):853-859. doi: 10.1111/jvim.16057. Epub 2021 Feb 3. PMID: 33534961; PMCID: PMC7995375.

17. Wasser S P. Current findings, future trends, and unsolved problems in studies of medicinal mushrooms. Appl Microbiol Biotechnol, 2011; 89: 1323-1332. https://doi.org/10.1007/s00253-010-3067-4

18. Brown D C, Reetz J. "Single Agent Polysaccharopeptide Delays Metastases and Improves Survival in Naturally Occurring Hemangiosarcoma", Evidence-Based Complementary and Alternative Medicine, 2012. Article ID 384301, 8 pages, 2012. https://doi.org/10.1155/2012/384301

19. Rathore H, Prasad S, Sharma S. Mushroom nutraceuticals for improved nutrition and better human health: A review, 2017. PharmaNutrition 5(2): 35-46. https://doi.org/10.1016/j.phanu.2017.02.001

20. Babu P D and Subhasree R S. The sacred mushroom "Reishi"-a review, 2008. American-Eurasian Journal of Botany, 1(3): 107-110.

21. Das S K, Masuda M, Sakurai A, Sakakibara M. Medicinal uses of the mushroom Cordyceps militaris: Current state and prospects, 2010. Fitoterapia, 81(8): 961-968. https://doi.org/10.1016/j.fitote.2010.07.010

22. Mehra A, Zaidi K U, Mani A, Thawani V. The health benefits of Cordyceps militaris—A review. Kavaka. 2017;48(1):27-32.

23. Kathy A and Eric Y. A Turkey Tails Polysaccharide as an Immunochemotherapy Agent in Cancer. *Alternative and Complementary Therapies. 2007; 178-182.* https://doi.org/10.1089/act.2007.13410

24. Kim G Y, Jeong H W, Jeong D J, Song H B, Lee H G. *Effects of Shiitake mushrooms on anti-platelet aggregation and anti-thrombotic. Journal of Physiology and Pathology in Korean Medicine. 2013, 27(2): 1738-7698 (pISSN).*

25. Friedman M. *Chemistry, Nutrition, and Health-Promoting Properties of Hericium erinaceus (Lion's Mane) Mushroom Fruiting Bodies and Mycelia and Their Bioactive Compounds. Journal of Agricultural and Food Chemistry. 2015; 63(32): 7108-7123.* https://doi.org/10.1021/acs.jafc.5b02914

26. Eid J I, Das B, Al-Tuwaijri M M, Basal W T. *Targeting SARS-COV-2 with Chaga Mushroom: An in silico study toward developing a natural antiviral compound. 2021; 9(21): 6513-6523.* https://doi.org/10.1002/fsn3.2576

27. Eid J I, Al-Tuwaijri M M, Mohanty S, Das B. *Chaga mushroom (Inonotus obliquus) polysaccharides exhibit genoprotective effects in UVB-exposed embryonic zebrafish (Danio rerio) through coordinated expression of DNA repair genes. 2021; (7)2: e06003.* https://doi.org/10.1016/j.heliyon.2021.e06003

28. Marco M L, Heeney D, Binda S, Cifelli C J, Cotter P D, Foligné B, Gänzle M, Kort R, Pasin G, Pihlanto A, Smid E J, Hutkins R. *Health benefits of fermented foods: microbiota and beyond. Current Opinion in Biotechnology. 2017; 44: 94-102.* https://doi.org/10.1016/j.copbio.2016.11.010

29. Kim D H, Jeong D, Kang I B, Lim H W, Cho Y J, Seo K H. *Modulation of the intestinal microbiota of dogs by*

kefir as a functional dairy product. *Journal of Dairy Science. 2019; 102(5): 3903-3911.*

30. Samanta S. Chapter 27 – Prospective role of prebiotics and probiotics in gut immunity. *Microbiome, Immunity, Digestive Health and Nutrition. 2022; 387-404.* https://doi.org/10.1016/B978-0-12-822238-6.00014-5

31. Syer S D, Wallace J L. Environmental and NSAID-Enteropathy: Dysbiosis as a Common Factor. *Curr Gastroenterol Rep. 2014; 16: 377.* https://doi.org/10.1007/s11894-014-0377-1

32. Wallace J L, Syer S, Denou E, de Palma G, Vong L, McKnight W, Jury J, Bolla M, Bercik P, Collins S M, Verdu E, Ongini E. Proton Pump Inhibitors Exacerbate NSAID-Induced Small Intestinal Injury by Inducing Dysbiosis. *Gastroenterology. 2011; 141(4): 1314-1322.e5.* https://doi.org/10.1053/j.gastro.2011.06.075

33. Monk J M, Zhang C P, Wu W, Zarepoor L, Lu J T, Liu R, Pauls K P, Wood G A, Tsao R, Robinson L E, Power K A. White and dark kidney beans reduce colonic mucosal damage and inflammation in response to dextran sodium sulfate. *The Journal Of Nutritional Biochemistry. 2015; 26(7): 752-760.* https://doi.org/10.1016/j.jnutbio.2015.02.003

34. El-Hack et al. Curcumin, the active substance of turmeric: its effect on health and ways to improve its bioavailability. *Journal of the Science of Food and Agriculture. 2021; 101(14): 5747-5762.* https://doi.org/10.1002/jsfa.11372

35. Ma Z, Wang N, He H, Tang X. Pharmaceutical strategies of improving oral systemic bioavailability of curcumin for clinical application. *Journal of Controlled Release. 2019; 316: 359-380.* https://doi.org/10.1016/j.jconrel.2019.10.053

36. *Ustun Alkan F, Anlas C, Cinar S, Yildirim F, Ustuner O, Bakirel T, Gurel A. Effects of curcmin in combination with cyclophosphamide on canine mammary cell lines. Veterinarni Medicina. 2014; 59(11): 553-572.*

37. *Kobatake Y, Nakata K, Sakai H, Sasaki, Yamato O, Takashim, S, Nishii N, Maeda S, Islam M S, Kamishina H. The Long-Term Clinical Course of Canine Degenerative Myelopathy and Therapeutic Potential of Curcumin. Vet. Sci. 2021; 8(9):192. https://doi.org/10.3390/vetsci8090192*

38. *Ayaz et al. Evaluation of the anthelmintic activity of pumpkin seeds (Cucurbita maxima) in mice naturally infected with aspiculuris tetraptera. Journal of Pharmacognosy and Phytotherapy. 2015; 7(9).*

23. INDEXES

A

B

C

P

Pancreatitis, 8, 40, 64
Pears, 26, 31, 64, 66
Peppermint, 31
Phlegm resolving, 29
Phycocyanin, 40, 41
Pickles, 50, 59
Pork, 28, 88, 90, 92
Post-natal, 19
Pre-natal, 19
Pumpkin, 30, 34, 54, 55, 56, 59, 75, 84, 99
Pumpkin seeds, 54
Pungent, 33, 55, 59

Q

Quail, 28, 90
Quinoa, 34

R

Rabbit, 28, 90, 92
Radish, 31, 62
Raw meaty bones, 36, 69, 70, 71, 79, 83, 85, 87, 88, 89
Reishi, 48, 49, 96

S

Salmon, 28, 90, 92
Salty, 33, 59
Sardines, 28, 90, 92
Sauerkraut, 50, 59
Seaweed, 31, 43, 59
Shark, 28, 90
Shiitake, 48, 49, 92, 97
Skin allergies, 2, 38, 49, 64
Sour, 33, 50, 59, 64
Spirulina, 38, 39, 40, 42, 57, 94
Stagnation moving, 29
Sunflower seeds, 34
Superfoods, 38
Sweet, 26, 33, 34, 59, 81, 84, 85

T

Tempeh, 50
Thyme, 11, 31
Thyroid function, 31, 41, 43
Traditional medicine, 9
Tuna, 28, 90
Turkey, 28, 48, 49, 88, 90, 96
Turkey Tail, 48, 49
Turmeric, 38, 52, 93

U

Urinary incontinence, 18, 51

V

Venison, 11, 29, 90, 92, 93

W

Water, 18
Wheat, 34
Wheatgrass, 58
White Baits, 28, 90
Wood, 17

Y

Yoghurt, 50, 53

Ingram Content Group Australia Pty Ltd
Printed in Australia
AUHW011002190723
381044AU00003B/3

9 780645 831801